THE PLAY

CHORD SONGBOOK 2

WISE PUBLICATIONS
part of The Music Sales Group
London / New York / Paris / Sydney / Copenhagen / Berlin / Madrid / Tokyo

Published by
Wise Publications
14-15 Berners Street, London, W1T 3LJ, UK.

Exclusive distributors:
Music Sales Limited, Distribution Centre, Newmarket Road,
Bury St Edmunds, Suffolk, IP33 3YB, UK.
Music Sales Pty Limited
120 Rothschild Avenue, Rosebery, NSW 2018, Australia.

Order No. AM987789 ISBN 1-84609-778-9

Edited by Tom Farncombe.
Printed in the EU.

www.musicsales.com

All Sparks

Words & Music by
Thomas Smith, Russell Leetch & Christopher Urbanowicz

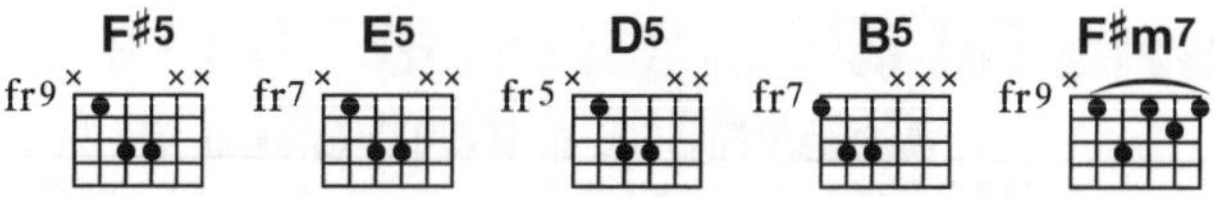

Intro

| 𝄆 F♯5 | F♯5 | F♯5 | F♯5 |
| E5 | E5 | F♯5 | F♯5 𝄇
(You're)

Verse 1

F♯5
You're answering questions that have not yet been asked.
E5 F♯5
All sparks will burn out in the end.

You burn like a bouncing cigarette on the road.
E5 F♯5
All sparks will burn out in the end.

Chorus 1

D5 F♯5 B5 D5
All sparks will burn out,
F♯5 B5 D5
All sparks will burn out,
F♯5 B5 D5 F♯5 B5
All sparks will burn out

In the end.

Link 1

| F♯5 | F♯5 | F♯5 | F♯5 |
| E5 | E5 | F♯5 | F♯5 ||
(You're)

Verse 2

F♯5
You're casting opinions at people who need them.
E5 F♯5
All sparks will burn out in the end.

Well be careful angel, this life is just too long.
E5 F♯5
All sparks will burn out in the end.

Chorus 2

As Chorus 1

Interlude

| F♯5 | F♯5 | F♯5 | F♯5 ‖

Link 2

| F♯5 | F♯5 | F♯5 | F♯5 |

| E5 | E5 | F♯5 | F♯5 ‖
(You)

Bridge

F♯5 E5 F♯5
You burn like a bouncing cigarette.

Chorus 3

D5 F♯5 B5 D5
All sparks will burn out,
F♯5 B5 D5
All sparks will burn out,
F♯5 B5 D5
All sparks will burn out,
F♯5 B5 D5
All sparks will burn out,
F♯5 B5 D5
All sparks will burn out,
F♯5 B5 D5
All sparks will burn out,
F♯5 B5 D5 F♯5 B5
All sparks will burn out,
F♯m7
In the end.

America

Song by Johnny Borrell & Andy Burrows
Music by Razorlight

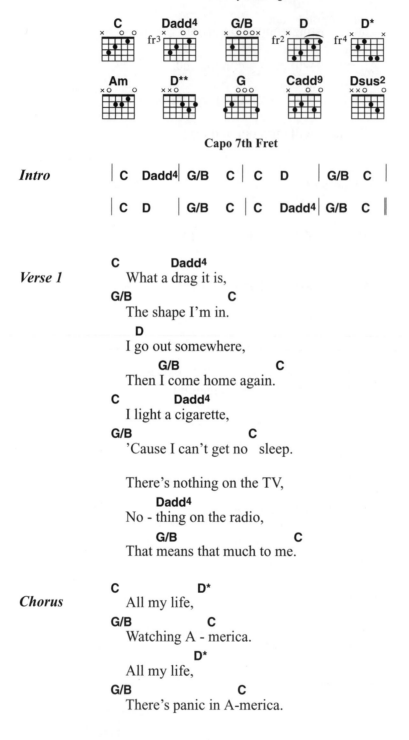

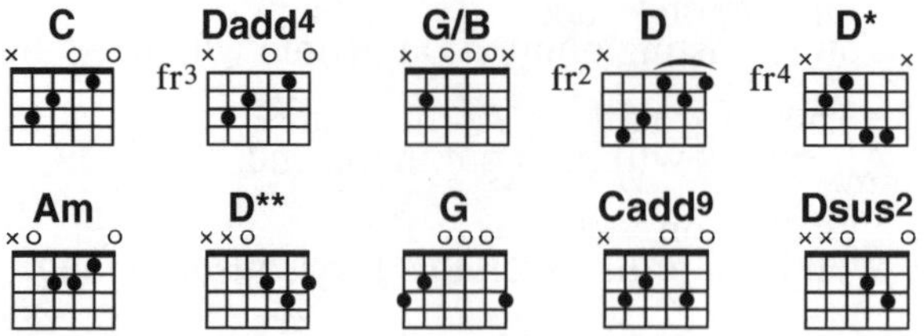

Capo 7th Fret

Intro

| C Dadd4 | G/B C | C D | G/B C |
| C D | G/B C | C Dadd4 | G/B C ||

Verse 1

C Dadd4
What a drag it is,
G/B C
The shape I'm in.
D
I go out somewhere,
G/B C
Then I come home again.
C Dadd4
I light a cigarette,
G/B C
'Cause I can't get no sleep.

There's nothing on the TV,
Dadd4
No - thing on the radio,
G/B C
That means that much to me.

Chorus

C D*
All my life,
G/B C
Watching A - merica.
D*
All my life,
G/B C
There's panic in A-merica.

Cont.

```
Am                D**
   Oh, oh, oh,    oh!
G                                  C
   There's trouble in A - merica.
Am                D**      G
   Oh, oh, oh,   oh.
```

Verse 2

```
C              Dadd4
   Yester - day was easy,
G/B                              C
Happiness came and went.
            D
I got the movie script,
       G/B                             C
But I don't know what it meant.
C              Dadd4
   I light a cigarette,
        G/B              C
Cause I can't get no   sleep.

There's no - thing on the TV,
       Dadd4
No - thing on the radio,
       G/B                            C
That means that much to me.

Nothing on the TV,
       Dadd4                          G/B                 C
No - thing on the radio, that I can believe in.
```

Chorus

```
C                  D*
   All my life,
G/B                C
   Watching A - merica.
               D*
   All my life,
G/B                          C
   There's panic in A - merica.
```

Cont.

```
Am              D**
   Oh, oh, oh,     oh!
G                           C
   There's trouble in A - merica.
Am              D**
   Oh, oh, oh,    oh!
G                           C
   There's trouble in A - merica.
Am              D**     G
   Oh, oh, oh,    oh!
```

Bridge

```
| C      D** | G          | C      D** | G          |
```

```
C            Dadd4
   Yester - day was easy
G/B                    C
Yes, I got the news.
C                  Dadd4
   Oh, when you get it straight,
            G/B                        C
You stand up you just can't lose.
                Dadd4
Give you my confidence,
G/B                Cadd9
All my faith in life.
       C
Don't stand me up,
       Dadd4
Don't let me down, no,
G/B                C
I need you tonight.
    C          Dsus2
To hold me,
G/B                 C
   Say you'll be here.
```

Cont.

```
        C           D**
And hold me,
G/B                     Cadd9
   Say you'll be here.
        C           D**
And hold me,
G/B              Cadd9
Say you'll be here.
C        D**    G/B    C
Hold.
```

Chorus

```
Am                D**
   All my life
G                     C
   I'm watching A - merica
Am                D**
   All my life,
G                         C
   There's panic in A - merica.
Am                D**
   Oh, oh, oh,     oh!
G                    C
   She's lost in A - merica.
Am                D**    G      C
   Oh, oh, oh,    oh.
                         Am       D**    G      C
Tell me how does it feel?
                         Am       D**    G      C
Tell me how does it feel?
                         Am       D**    G
Tell me how does it feel?
```

Outro

```
| C   Dadd4 | G/B   Cadd9 | C    D     | G6/B    Cadd9 |

| C   Dadd4 | G/B   Cadd9 | C    Dadd4 | G/B    C      |

| G/B     C | G/B     C   | G/B     C  ||
```

Bang Bang You're Dead

Words & Music by
David Hammond, Carl Barat, Anthony Rossomando & Gary Powell

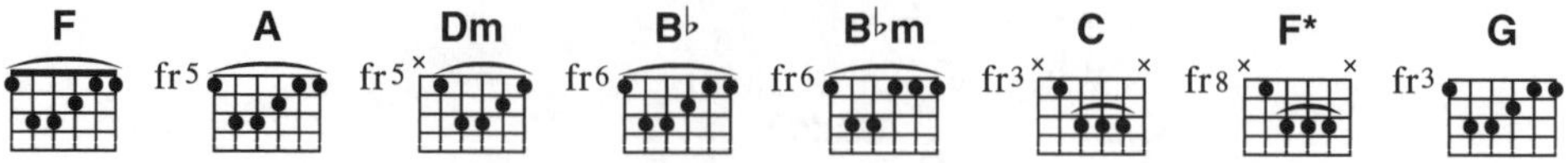

Intro

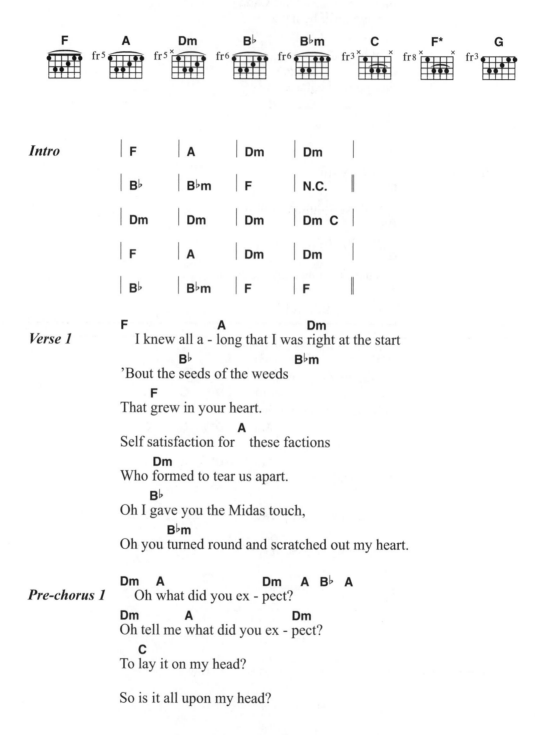

F	A	Dm	Dm
B♭	B♭m	F	N.C.	
Dm	Dm	Dm	Dm C
F	A	Dm	Dm
B♭	B♭m	F	F	

Verse 1

F A Dm
I knew all a - long that I was right at the start
B♭ B♭m
'Bout the seeds of the weeds
F
That grew in your heart.
A
Self satisfaction for these factions
Dm
Who formed to tear us apart.
B♭
Oh I gave you the Midas touch,
B♭m
Oh you turned round and scratched out my heart.

Pre-chorus 1

Dm A Dm A B♭ A
Oh what did you ex - pect?
Dm A Dm
Oh tell me what did you ex - pect?
C
To lay it on my head?

So is it all upon my head?

```
             F        A              Dm
*Chorus 1*     Bang bang, you're dead,
             B♭          A     F
             Always so easily led.
                  A             Dm
             Bang bang, you're dead,
             B♭          A            F*
             Put all the rumours to bed.
                  A             Dm    C
             Bang bang, you're dead.

             F                 A               Dm
*Verse 2*      I knew all a - long, but I was loathe to believe
                       B♭                     B♭m
             There was nothing but spite, fury and lies.
                     F
             Oh the webs that you weave.
                       A                       Dm
             An illusion to a conclusion, and oh, it's oh so tawdry.
                       B♭
             When you put it to bed, kick it in the head,
             B♭m
             Oh won't they just let it be.
```

Bridge	Dm G	G	Dm A	A	
	Dm G	G	Dm A	A B♭ A	A B♭ A ‖

```
             F        A              Dm
*Chorus 2*     Bang bang, you're dead,
             B♭          A     F
             Always so easily led.
                  A             Dm
             Bang bang, you're dead,
             B♭          A            F
             Put all the rumours to bed.
                  A             Dm    C
             Bang bang, you're dead.
```

Guitar solo	F	A	Dm	Dm
	B♭	B♭m	F	F ‖

```
              Dm   A                     Dm    A  B♭  A
Pre-chorus 2     Oh what did you ex - pect?
              Dm          A                    Dm
              Oh tell me what did you ex - pect?
                 C
              To lay it on my head?

              So is it all upon my head?

              F         A                 Dm
Chorus 3         Bang bang, you're dead,
              B♭          A        F
              Always so easily led.
                   A                Dm
              Bang bang, you're dead,
              B♭            A                 F
              Put all the rumours to bed.
                   A                Dm
              Bang bang, you're dead.
                   F*           A               B♭
              Bang bang, bang bang, you're dead,
              B♭m         F
              Oh you're dead.
```

Because I Want You

Words & Music by
Brian Molko, Stefan Olsdal & Steve Hewitt

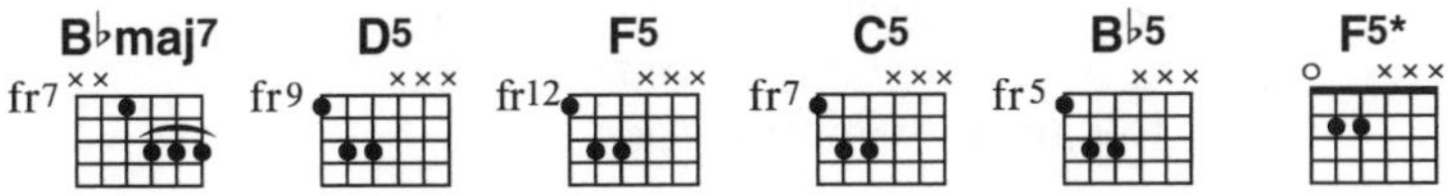

⑥ = F ③ = A♭
⑤ = B♭ ② = C
④ = E♭ ① = C

Verse 1

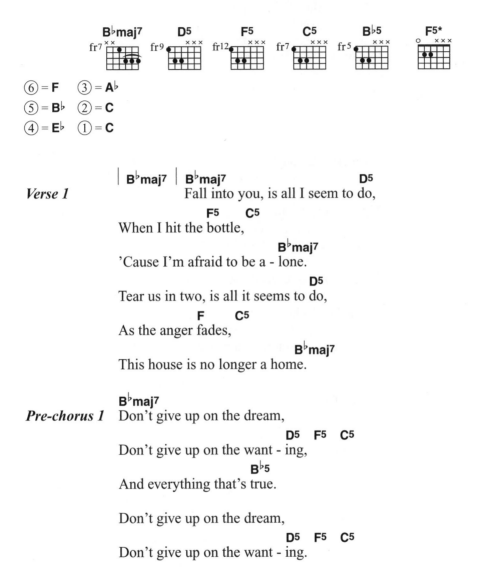

| B♭maj7 | B♭maj7 D5
Fall into you, is all I seem to do,
F5 C5
When I hit the bottle,
B♭maj7
'Cause I'm afraid to be a - lone.
D5
Tear us in two, is all it seems to do,
F C5
As the anger fades,
B♭maj7
This house is no longer a home.

Pre-chorus 1

B♭maj7
Don't give up on the dream,
D5 F5 C5
Don't give up on the want - ing,
B♭5
And everything that's true.

Don't give up on the dream,
D5 F5 C5
Don't give up on the want - ing.

```
              C5                F5*
Chorus 1      Because I want you too.

              Because I want you too.
                                Bb5
              Because I want you too.

              Because I want you.

              Because I want you.

              | Bbmaj7 | Bbmaj7                    D5
Verse 2                  Stumble into you, is all I ever do,
                          F5    C5
              My memory's hazy,
                                     Bbmaj7
              And I'm afraid to be a - lone.
                                          D5
              Tear us in two, is all it's gonna do,
                            F5    C5
              As the headache fades,
                                           Bbmaj7
              This house is no longer a home.


Pre-chorus 2  As Chorus 1


Chorus 2      As Chorus 1
```

Chorus 3

```
F5*
   Because I want you too.
                        B♭5
Because I want you too.

Because I want you.

Because I want you.
```

Verse 3

```
| B♭maj7 | B♭maj7                    D5
               Fall into you is all I ever do,
                        F5      C5
When I hit the bot - tle,
                               B♭maj7
'Cause I'm afraid to be a - lone.

Tear us in two,
          D5        F5      C5
Tear us in two,

Tear us in two.
```

Chorus 4

```
F5*
   Because I want you too.
                        B♭5
Because I want you    too.

Because I want you.
                          F5*
Because I want you.

Because I want you too.
                        B♭5
Because I want you    too.

Because I want you.
                          F5*
Because I want you.
```

Burn The Witch

Words & Music by
Josh Homme, Joey Castillo & Troy Van Leeuwen

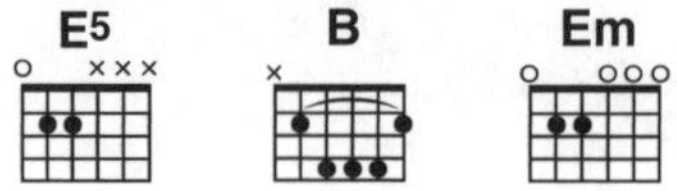

Intro |: E5 | E5 :| *Play 6 times*

Verse 1

E5
Holding hands, skipping like a stone.

On our way, to see what we have done.

The first to speak, is the first to lie.

The children cross their heats and hope to die.

Chorus 1

B Em B
Bite your tongue,
Em B Em B Em
Swear to keep your mouth shut.

Interlude |: E5 | E5 | E5 | E5 :| *Play 8 times*

Verse 2

E5
Ask yourself, will I burn in Hell?

Then write it down, and cast it in the well.

There they are, the mob it cries for blood.

To twist the tale, into firewood.

Fan the flames, with a little lie.

Then turn your cheek, until the fire dies.

The skin it peels, like the truth, away.

What it was, I will never say. Ah, oh. Ah, oh.

```
                 B        Em     B          Em
Chorus 2          Bite your tongue, swear to keep,
                  B       Em
                 Keep your mouth shut.
                 B       Em
                 Make up something,
                 B       Em        E5
                 Make up something good.

Interlude 2      |: E5 :|  Play 5 times

Guitar Solo      |: E5 :|  Play 16 times

                 E5
Chorus 3         Holding hands, skipping like a stone.

                 Burn the witch, burn to ash and bone.

                 Burn the witch, burn to ash and bone.

                 Burn the witch, burn to ash and bone.

                    E5
Outro            |: Oh.  :|  Play 12 times
```

Cellphone's Dead

Words & Music by
Beck

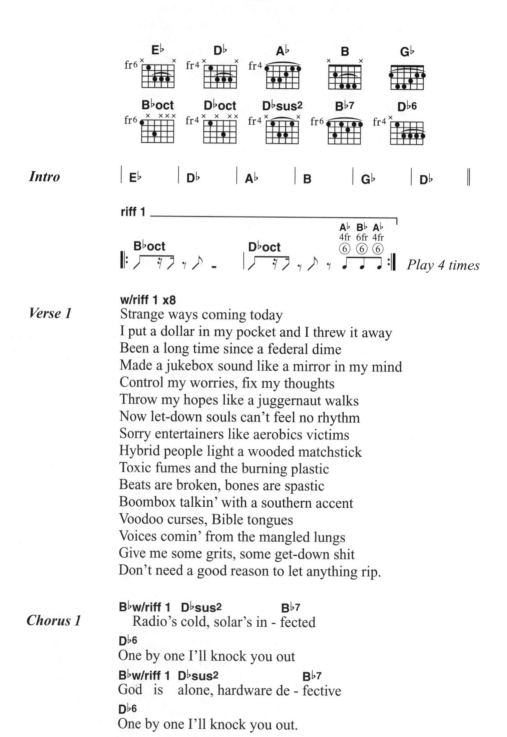

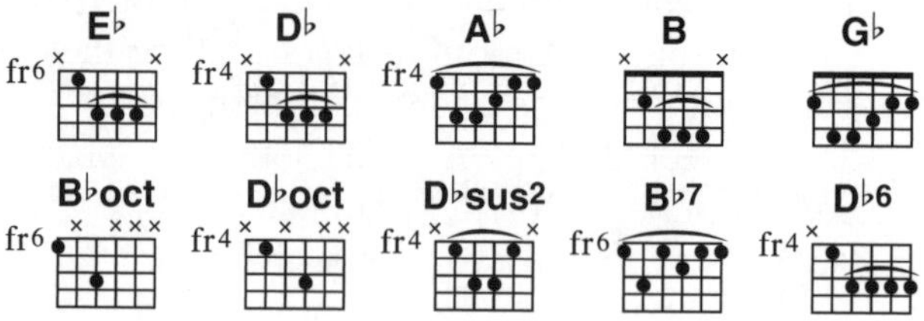

Intro | E♭ | D♭ | A♭ | B | G♭ | D♭ ||

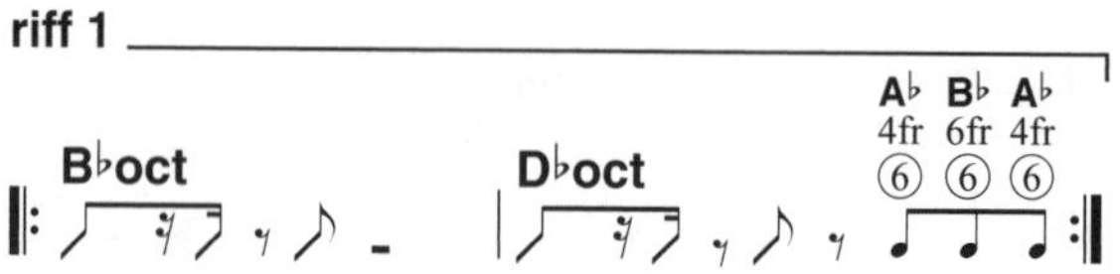

Play 4 times

Verse 1
w/riff 1 x8
Strange ways coming today
I put a dollar in my pocket and I threw it away
Been a long time since a federal dime
Made a jukebox sound like a mirror in my mind
Control my worries, fix my thoughts
Throw my hopes like a juggernaut walks
Now let-down souls can't feel no rhythm
Sorry entertainers like aerobics victims
Hybrid people light a wooded matchstick
Toxic fumes and the burning plastic
Beats are broken, bones are spastic
Boombox talkin' with a southern accent
Voodoo curses, Bible tongues
Voices comin' from the mangled lungs
Give me some grits, some get-down shit
Don't need a good reason to let anything rip.

Chorus 1
B♭w/riff 1 D♭sus2 B♭7
Radio's cold, solar's in - fected
D♭6
One by one I'll knock you out
B♭w/riff 1 D♭sus2 B♭7
God is alone, hardware de - fective
D♭6
One by one I'll knock you out.

Verse 2

w/riff 1 x8
Mr. Microphone making all the damage felt
Like a laser manifesto make a mannequin melt
There's people phonin' in like it's unlimited minutes
Going through the motions just to savour they did it
Treadmill's running underneath their feet
So they feel like they're going somewhere but they're not
So let's put boots on the warehouse floor
Comin' to you like a rope on a chainstore
Throwing equipment from a moving van
Grab a microphone like a utility man
Now fix the beat, now break the rest
Make a kick drum sound like an S.O.S.
Get a tow-truck 'cause it's after dark
And the dance floor's full but everybody's double-parked!

Link

| **E♭** | **D♭** | **A♭** | **B** | **G♭** | **D♭** ||

Chorus 2

B♭w/riff 1 D♭sus2 B♭7
Cell phone's dead, lost in the desert
D♭6
One by one I'll knock you out
B♭w/riff 1 D♭sus2 B♭7
Eye of the sun is out of its socket
D♭6
One by one I'll knock you out.

Breakdown

| **B♭w/riff 1** | **D♭** | **B♭** | **D♭** |
One by one
B♭ | **D♭** | **B♭** | **D♭** |
This jam is real... that's right.

||: **B♭w/riff 1** | **D♭** | **B♭** | [1, 2.] **D♭** :||
(3°) Eye of the sun, eye of the sun. Eye of the

[3.] | **D♭** ||
sun. Eye of the

Outro

||: **E♭** | **D♭** | **A♭** | **B** | **G♭** | **D♭** :||
sun. *Play 6 times*
(3°-6°) Ah.______ Ah.______ Ah.______

| **E♭** (fermata) **D♭** (fermata) ||

Cheated Hearts

Words & Music by
Nicholas Zinner, Brian Chase & Karen Orzolek

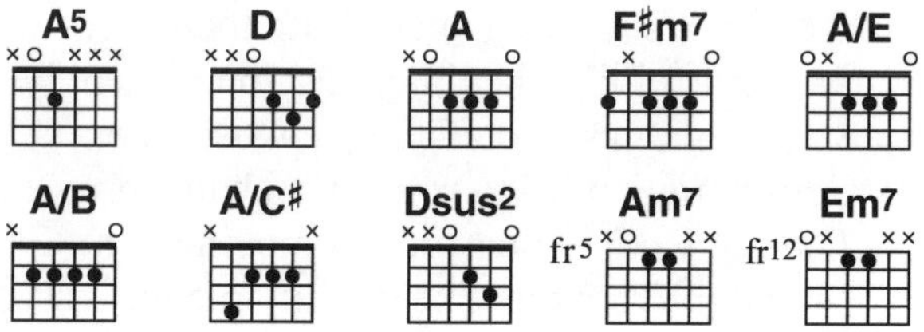

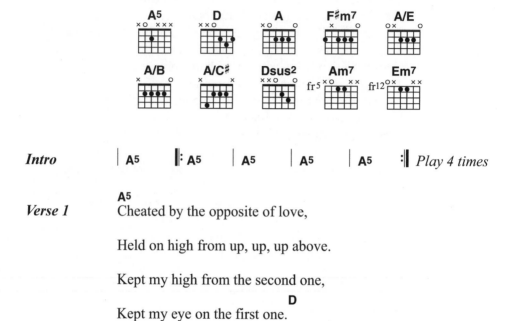

Intro | A5 |: A5 | A5 | A5 | A5 :| *Play 4 times*

Verse 1

```
A5
Cheated by the opposite of love,

Held on high from up, up, up above.

Kept my high from the second one,
                                D
Kept my eye on the first one.
```

Chorus 1

```
      A
Now take these rings and stow them safe away,
    F♯m7
I'll wear them on another rainy day.
A/E
Take these rings and stow them safe away,
    F♯m7                        D
I'll wear them on another rain - y day.
A
Take these rings and stow them safe away,
    F♯m7
I'll wear them on another rainy day.
A/E
Take these rings and stow them safe away,
    F♯m7
I'll wear them on another rainy day.
```

Link 1 | A | A/B | A | A/B ||
(Well I'm)

Verse 2

```
          A
Well I'm take-a, take-a, take-a, take-a, takin' it off.
            A/B
And she's take-a, take-a, take-a, take-a, takin' it off.
           A/C#
And he's take-a, take-a, take-a, take-a, takin' it off.
              Dsus2       D
And we're take-a, take-a, take-a, take-a, takin' it off.
```

Bridge 1

```
         A                                      A/B
Some - times I think that I'm bigger than the sound.
                                        A/C#
Well I think that I'm bigger than the sound.
                                        D
Well I think that I'm bigger than the sound.
                                        (Am7)
Well I think that I'm bigger than the sound.
```

Interlude 1 | Am7 | Em7 | Am7 | Em7 |
| Am7 | Em7 | Am7 | Em7 ||

Bridge 2

```
A        A/B        A
   Ooh,___ ooh.___
        A/B        A
Ooh,___ ooh.___
        A/B        A
Ooh,___ ooh.___
        A/B        A
Ooh,___ ooh.___
       A    A/B  A    A/B
She'll take on    high
       A    A/B       F#m7  A/E
She'll take on    high.
```

Bridge 3

```
      A                         A/B                F#m7
Some - times I think that I'm bigger than the sound.
                          A/B               A
Well I think that I'm bigger than the sound.
                          A/B               F#m7
Well I think that I'm bigger than the sound.
                          A/E               A5
Well I think that I'm bigger than the sound.
```

Link 2

||: A5 | A5 | A5 | A5 :||

Verse 3

As Verse 1

Chorus 2

As Chorus 1

Outro

||: Am7 | Em7 | Am7 | Em7 :||

Dance, Dance

Words & Music by
Peter Wentz, Andrew Hurley, Joseph Trohman & Patrick Stumph

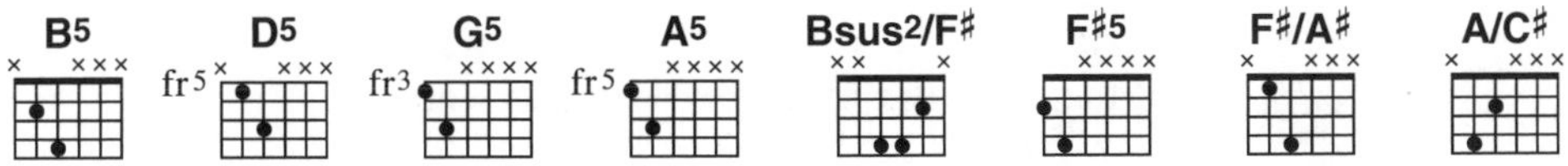

Drums
| 2 ||

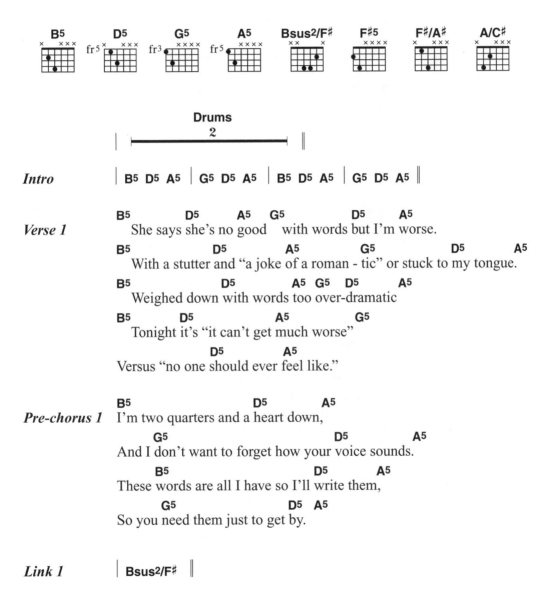

Intro | B5 D5 A5 | G5 D5 A5 | B5 D5 A5 | G5 D5 A5 ||

Verse 1
B5 D5 A5 G5 D5 A5
She says she's no good with words but I'm worse.
B5 D5 A5 G5 D5 A5
With a stutter and "a joke of a roman - tic" or stuck to my tongue.
B5 D5 A5 G5 D5 A5
Weighed down with words too over-dramatic
B5 D5 A5 G5
Tonight it's "it can't get much worse"
D5 A5
Versus "no one should ever feel like."

Pre-chorus 1
B5 D5 A5
I'm two quarters and a heart down,
G5 D5 A5
And I don't want to forget how your voice sounds.
B5 D5 A5
These words are all I have so I'll write them,
G5 D5 A5
So you need them just to get by.

Link 1 | Bsus2/F♯ ||

Chorus 1

```
B5          D5
   Dance, dance,
          G5            F#5     F#/A#B5
We're falling a - part to half  time.
          D5
Dance, dance,
      G5               F#5              F#/A#   B5
And these are the lives you'd love to lead.
          D5                 G5          F#5
Dance, this is the way     they'd love,
  F#/A#B5              D5        G5            F#5   F#/A#
If they knew how misery loved me.
```

Link 2

| B5 D5 A5 | G5 D5 A5 | B5 D5 A5 | G5 D5 A5 ||

Verse 2

```
B5  N.C.                        G5                 D5     A5
      You always fold just before you're found out,
B5              D5
   Drink up its last call, last resort,
G5                D5           A5
   But only the first mis - take and I.
```

Pre-chorus 2 As Pre-chorus 1

Bridge 1

```
B5          D5           A5  G5       D5
Why don't you show me, little bit of spine,
A5              N.C.
You've been saving for his mattress, love.
```

Chorus 2 As Chorus 1

Bridge 2

```
| B5        | A/C#      | F#5       | G5        ||

B5                              A/C#
Why don't you show me the little bit of spine,
               F#5                  G5
You've been saving for his mattress.
B5                          A/C#
   I only want sympa - thy in the form of you
F#5                        G5   F#5
Crawling into bed with me.
```

Link

```
| F#5       | F#5       ||
```

Chorus 3

```
B5        D5
   Dance, dance,
      G5          F#5      F#/A# B5
We're falling a - part to half   time.
        D5
Dance, dance,
    G5             F#5           F#/A#  B5
And these are the lives you'd love to lead.
B5        D5        G5            F#5  F#/A#
   Dance this is the way they'd love.
B5        D5        G5            F#5  F#/A#
   Dance this is the way they'd love.
B5        D5        G5            F#5  F#/A#
   Dance this is the way they'd love.
  F#/A# B5          D5      G5          F#5  F#/A#
If they knew how misery loved me.
```

Outro

```
| B5 D5 A5 | G5 D5 A5 | B5 D5 A5 | G5 D5 A5 ||

B5         D5      A5
   Dance, dance.
G5         D5      A5
   Dance, dance.
B5         D5      A5
   Dance, dance.
G5         D5      A5
   Dance, dance.
```

Dirty Little Secret

Words & Music by
Tyson Ritter & Nick Wheeler

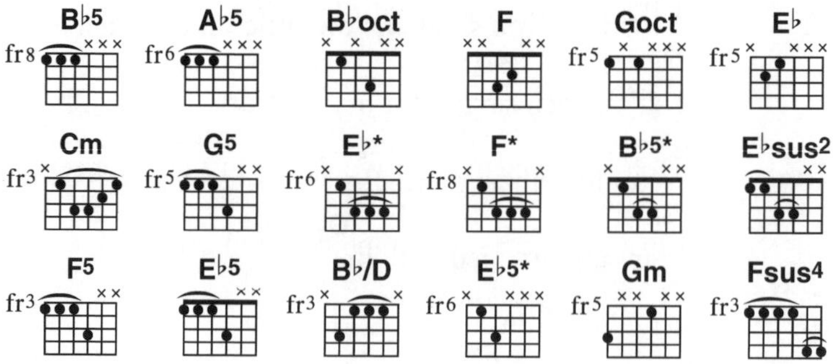

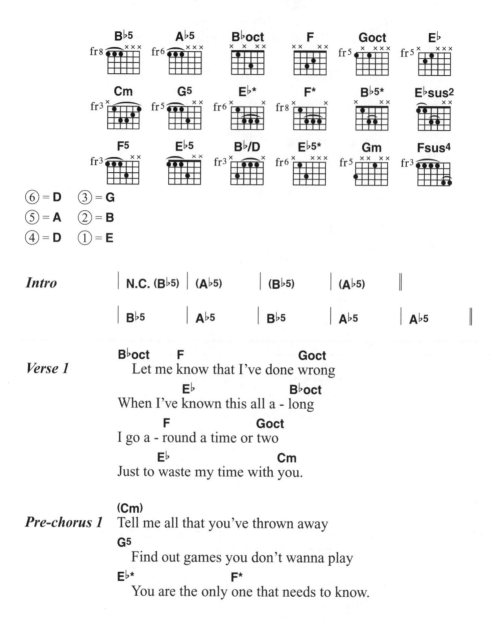

⑥ = D ③ = G
⑤ = A ② = B
④ = D ① = E

Intro | N.C. (B♭5) | (A♭5) | (B♭5) | (A♭5) ||

| B♭5 | A♭5 | B♭5 | A♭5 | A♭5 ||

Verse 1
B♭oct F Goct
Let me know that I've done wrong
E♭ B♭oct
When I've known this all a - long
F Goct
I go a - round a time or two
E♭ Cm
Just to waste my time with you.

Pre-chorus 1
(Cm)
Tell me all that you've thrown away
G5
Find out games you don't wanna play
E♭* F*
You are the only one that needs to know.

Chorus 1

B♭5* E♭sus2
I'll keep you my dirty little secret
G5 F5
(Dirty little secret——)
B♭5* E♭sus2
Don't tell any - one or you'll be just another regret
G5 F5
(Just another regret, hope that you can keep it)
E♭sus2
My dirty little secret.

Verse 2

B♭5 F5 G5
Who has to know when we live such fragile lives
E♭5 B♭5
It's the best way we sur - vive
F5 G5
I go a - round a time or two
E♭5 Cm
Just to waste my time with you.

Pre-chorus 2 As Pre-chorus 1

Chorus 2 As Chorus 1

Bridge

G5
Who has to know

E♭sus2
The way she feels inside (in - side)

G5
Those thoughts I can't deny (de - ny)

E♭sus2
These sleeping dogs won't lie (won't lie)

And all I've tried to hide
B♭/D
It's eating me apart
Cm
Trace this life out.——

Link ‖: **B♭5** | **A♭5** | **B♭5** | **A♭5** :‖

Chorus 3

B♭oct **E♭5***
I'll keep you my dirty little secret
Gm **F5**
(Dirty little secret___)
B♭oct **E♭5**
Don't tell any - one or you'll be just another regret
Gm **F5**
(Just another regret.___)

Chorus 4

B♭5* **E♭sus2**
I'll keep you my dirty little secret
G5 **F5**
(Dirty little secret___)
B♭5* **E♭sus2**
Don't tell any - one or you'll be just another regret
G5 **F5**
(Just another regret, hope that you can keep it)
E♭sus2
My dirty little secret
F5 **G5**
Dirty little secret, dirty little secret
A♭5 **(B♭5)** **(A♭5)**
Who has to know?
| **B♭5** | **A♭5** **Fsus4** (fermata) ‖
Who has to know?___

The Fallen

Words & Music by
Alexander Kapranos, Nicholas McCarthy, Robert Hardy & Paul Thomson

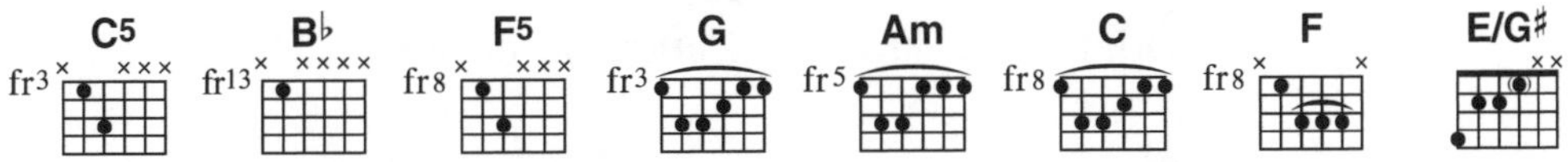

Intro

C5	C5	C5	C5 B♭ F5	C5 B♭ F5
C5 B♭ F5	C5 B♭ F5	C5 B♭ F5	C5 B♭ F5	
G	Am	C	G	
:Am F	Am F	Am F	G E/G♯:	

Verse 1

Am F Am
So they say you're a troubled boy,
F
Just because you like to destroy
Am F
All the things that bring the idiots joy.
G E/G♯ Am
Well, what's wrong with a little destruction?

And the Kunst won't talk to you,
Am F
'Cause you kissed St. Rollox adieu,
Am F
'Cause you robbed a super - market or two.
G E/G♯
Well, who gives a damn about the prophets of Tesco?

Chorus 1

C5 B♭ F5
Did I see you in a limou - sine,
C5 B♭ F5
Flinging out the fish and the unleav - ened?
C5 B♭ F5
Turn the rich into wine, as you walk on the mean.
G Am
Well the fallen are the virtuous among us,
C G
Walk a - mong us, never judge us.

Yeah we're all...

Verse 2

```
Am                F           Am
   Up now and get 'em, boy,
              F
Up now and get 'em, boy.
G                        E/G♯
Drink to the devil and death to the doctors!
```

Chorus 2

```
C5                       B♭      F5
   Did I see you in a limou - sine,
C5                                   B♭        F5
Flinging out the fish and the unleav - ened? Well,
G                    E/G♯        Am
   Five thousand users fed to - day.
             C                      G                (Am)
Oh, as you feed us won't you lead us to be blessed
           C                 G
```

Link 1

| Am F | Am F | Am F | G E/G♯ ‖

Verse 3

```
Am                    F
   So we stole and drank champagne,
          Am                             F
On the seventh seal you said you never feel pain.
   Am                             F
"I never feel pain, won't you hit me again?"
   G                                      E/G♯
"I need a bit of black and blue to be a rotation"
Am                  F
   In my blood I felt bubbles burst,
              Am                 F
There was a flash of fist, an eyebrow burst.
          Am               F
You've a lazy laugh and a red white shirt,
  G                E/G♯                   (C5)
I fall to the floor fainting at the sight of blood.
```

Chorus 3

```
C5                       B♭      F5
   Did I see you in a limou - sine,
C5                                   B♭        F5
Flinging out the fish and the unleav - ened?
              C5                 B♭              F5
You turn the rich into wine, walk on the mean.
         C5                                 B♭        F5
Be they Magdalen at Virgin you've already been,
         C5                            B♭       F5
You've already been and we've already seen
          G                Am
That the fallen are the virtuous among us,
          C                      G              C
Walk a - mong us, never judge us to be blessed
```

Bridge

G   C G
La la la la la la la

F   C   F
La la la la la

         C   G
La la la la la la la la.

Verse 4

Am   F
  So I'm sorry if I ever resisted,

 Am   F
I never had a doubt you ever existed.

 Am   F
I only have a problem when people insist on

G   E/G♯   Am
Taking their hate and placing it on your name.

                     F
So they say you're troubled boy,

Am   F
Just because you like to destroy.

    Am   F
You are the word, the word is 'destroy',

 G   E/G♯
I break this bottle, think of you fondly.

Chorus 4

C5   B♭   F5
  Did I see you in a limou - sine,

C5   B♭   F5
Flinging out the fish and the unleav - ened?

      C5   B♭   F5
To the whore in a hostel or the scum of a scheme.

         C5   B♭   F5
Turn the rich into wine, walk on the mean.

         C5   B♭   F5
It's not a jag in the arm, it's a nail in the beam.

        C5   B♭   F5
On this barren Earth you scatter your seed.

        C5   B♭   F5
Be they Magdelan or Virgin, you've already been.

                                 B♭   F5
You've already been and you've already seen, but the...

Outro

  C5   B♭   F5
𝄆 Wahoo!   𝄇 *Play 8 times*

                    C5   B♭   F5
Yeah! You've al - ready been, you've al - ready seen

        G   Am   C
That the fallen are the virtuous among us, walk a - mong us.

         G   C
Oh if you judge us we're all damned.

Four Kicks

Words & Music by
Jared Followill, Matthew Followill, Ivan Followill & Anthony Followill

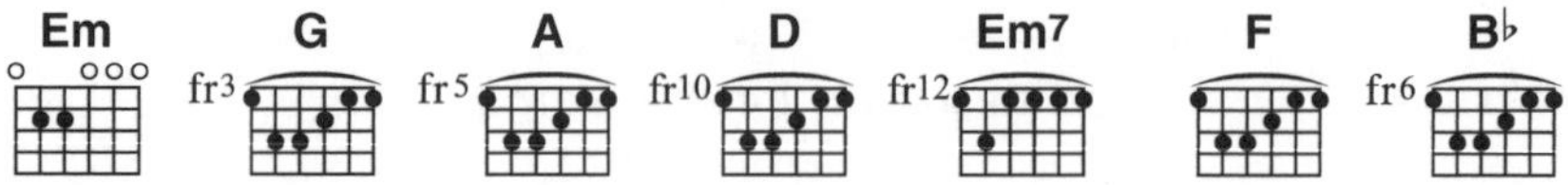

Intro |: Em G A G | Em G A G | Em G A G | D :|

Verse 1

Em7 ... Em G A G Em G A G
Huffman don't take no nonsense,
D ... Em G A G Em G A G
He's here to rectify.
Em7 ... Em G A G Em G A G
He's got his black belt buckle,
D ... Em G A G Em G A G
And the red man's fire in his eye.

Chorus 1

F ... B♭
You with your switchblade posse,
F
I'll get my guns from south.
B♭
We'll take to the yard like a cockfight,
Four kicks, whose strutting now.

Link 1 |: Em G A G | Em G A G | Em G A G | D :|

Verse 2

```
Em7                             Em  G  A  G  Em  G  A  G
   This party is overrated,
D                                   Em  G  A  G  Em  G  A  G
   But there ain't shit else to do.
Em7                                          Em  G  A  G  Em  G  A  G
   She's a lovin' on the boy from the city,
D                                       Em  G  A  G  Em  G  A  G
   I'll be lovin' him under my shoe.
```

Chorus 2

```
F                                         B♭
   You with your switchblade posse,
                                  F
I'll get my guns from south.
                                            B♭
We'll take to the yard like a cockfight,

Four kicks, whose strutting now.
```

Play 4 times

Solo

```
||: Em  G  A  G  | Em  G  A  G  | Em  G  A  G  | D  :||
```

Outro

```
F                                         B♭
   You with your switchblade posse,
                                  F
I'll get my guns from south.
                                            B♭
We'll take to the yard like a cockfight,
                  N.C.
Four kicks, whose strutting now.
```

The Great Escape

Words & Music by
Keith Murray, Christopher Cain & Michael Tapper

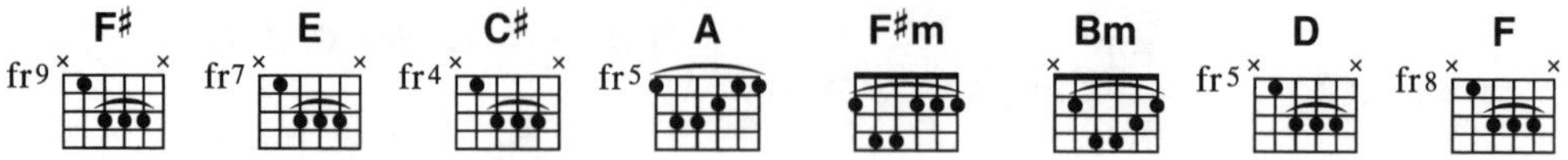

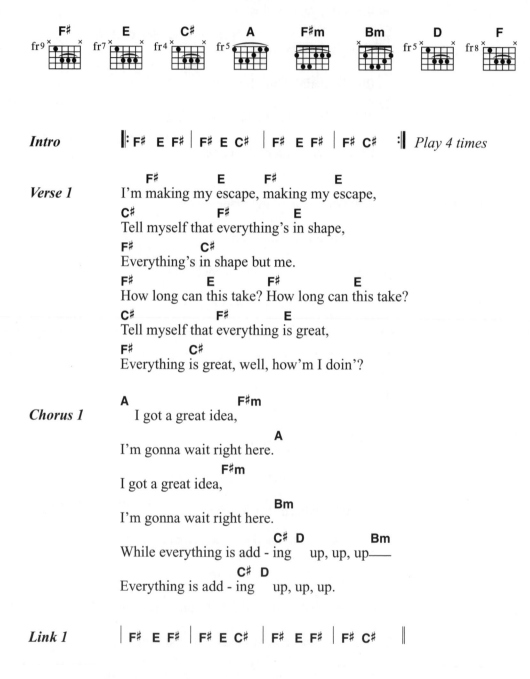

Intro ‖: F♯ E F♯ | F♯ E C♯ | F♯ E F♯ | F♯ C♯ :‖ *Play 4 times*

Verse 1

        F♯   E   F♯   E
I'm making my escape, making my escape,
C♯   F♯   E
Tell myself that everything's in shape,
F♯   C♯
Everything's in shape but me.
F♯   E   F♯   E
How long can this take? How long can this take?
C♯   F♯   E
Tell myself that everything is great,
F♯   C♯
Everything is great, well, how'm I doin'?

Chorus 1

A   F♯m
   I got a great idea,
                                            A
I'm gonna wait right here.
                              F♯m
I got a great idea,
                                            Bm
I'm gonna wait right here.
                                            C♯ D   Bm
While everything is add - ing   up, up, up——
                                  C♯ D
Everything is add - ing   up, up, up.

Link 1 | F♯ E F♯ | F♯ E C♯ | F♯ E F♯ | F♯ C♯ ‖

Verse 2

```
F#                E            F#               E
Breakin' both my hands, breakin' both my hands,
C#                F#             E
Tellin' me to take it like a man,
F#              C#
Take it like a man, I can't.
F#                E             F#               E
I don't un - derstand, I don't un - derstand,
C#                               F#          E
Please repeat what - ever you just said,
F#                     C#
Nothin's mak - in' sense, well, how'm I doin'?
```

Chorus 2 As Chorus 1

Interlude

```
||: F#  E  F# | F#  E  C# | F#  E  F# | F#  C#  :||
```

Solo

```
| D   | D   | Bm  | Bm  |
| D   | D   | Bm  | Bm  |
| A   | A   | Bm  | Bm  |
| D   | D   | E   | F   ||
```

Link 2

```
| F#  E  F# | F#  E  C# | F#  E  F# | F#  C#  ||
```

Verse 3

```
             F#               E                     F#               E
They're breakin' both my hands, they're breakin' both my hands,
             C#              F#          E
They're tellin' me to take it like a man,
F#               C#
Take it like a man, well fuck that.
F#                 E                   F#                 E
I don't un - derstand, said I don't un - derstand,
        C#                             F#          E
Said please repeat what - ever you just said,
           F#                   C#
'Cause nothin's mak - in' sense, well, how'm I doin'?
```

Chorus 3 As Chorus 1

Hands

Words & Music by
Brendan Benson & Jack White

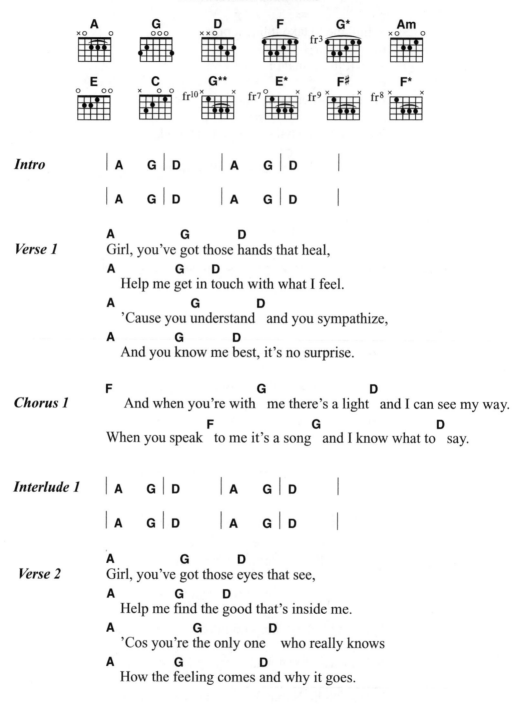

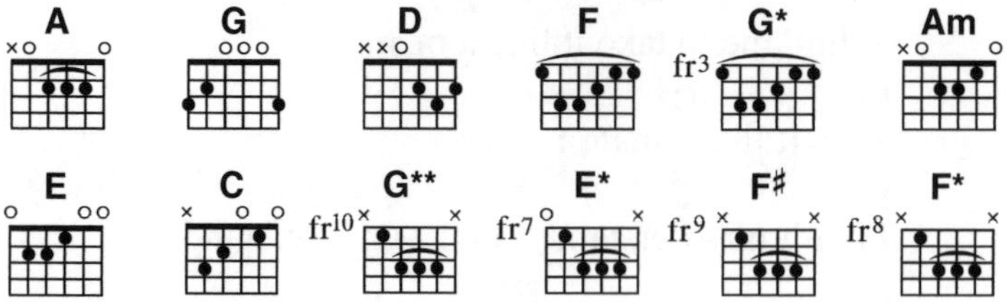

Intro

| A G | D | A G | D |

| A G | D | A G | D |

Verse 1

A G D
Girl, you've got those hands that heal,
A G D
Help me get in touch with what I feel.
A G D
'Cause you understand and you sympathize,
A G D
And you know me best, it's no surprise.

Chorus 1

F G D
And when you're with me there's a light and I can see my way.
F G D
When you speak to me it's a song and I know what to say.

Interlude 1

| A G | D | A G | D |

| A G | D | A G | D |

Verse 2

A G D
Girl, you've got those eyes that see,
A G D
Help me find the good that's inside me.
A G D
'Cos you're the only one who really knows
A G D
How the feeling comes and why it goes.

Chorus 2 As Chorus 1

Interlude 2

```
| (D) N.C. | (E)      | (E)      | (E)      |

| (D)      | (C)      | (G)      ||
```

Verse 1

```
(E)
   Ooh ooh ooh ooh,
(D)
   Ooh ooh ooh ooh,
(C)
   Ooh ooh ooh ooh,
(G)
   Ooh ooh ooh ooh.
```

Outro Chorus

```
E                      D                   G
    When you're with   me there's a light

And I can see my way.
E                     D                   C
    When you speak    to me it's a song
                          G        G** F# F*
And I know what to    say.
E                 D                     C
    When you lis - ten there's a hope
                         G              G** F# F*
And I know I'm be - ing heard.
E                     D                      C
    When you smile    at me and I know
                                 G           G** F# F*
That we don't have to speak    a word.
E                      D                     C
    When you're with   me there's a light
                    G           G** F# F*
And I can see    my way.
E                     D                   C
    When you speak    to me it's a song
                       G          G** F# F*
And I know what    to say.
```

```
| E* (fermata) | N.C.     ||
```

Get Myself Into It

Words & Music by
Luke Jenner, Vito Roccoforte & Matthew Safer

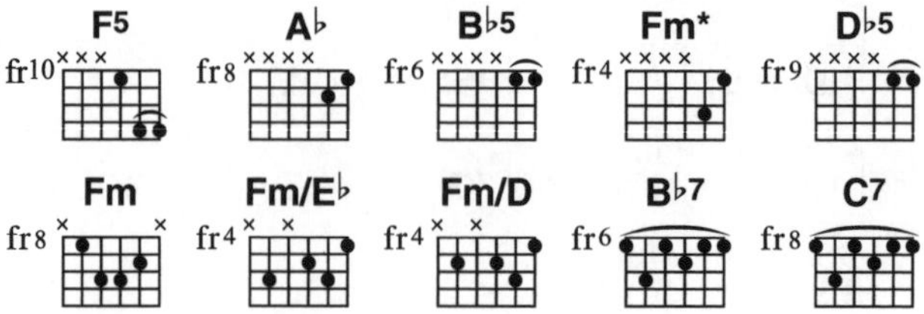

Intro ||: N.C. (F5) | (F5) | (F5) | (F5) :||

Verse 1

F5
Ho - li - day

Get a - way

I feel fine

And children's minded.

Chorus 1

Fm w/riff 1
Got to get myself into it

B♭7
Got to get myself into it

Fm
Got to get myself into it

B♭7
Why not help me do it?

Fm
Got to get myself into it

B♭7
Got to get myself into it

Fm
Got to get myself into it

B♭7 **C7** **N.C.(Fm)**
Why not help me do it?

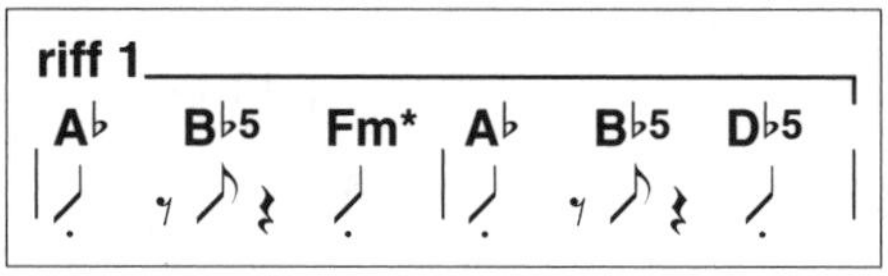

Link Hey! Hey! Hey! Hey! Hey! Hey! Hey!

Verse 2

F5
Don't be late

At God's gate

Don't talk shit

Out with it.

Chorus 2

Fm w/riff 1
Got to get myself into it
B♭7
Got to get myself into it
Fm
Got to get myself into it
B♭7
Why not help me do it?
Fm
Got to get myself into it
B♭7
Got to get myself into it
Fm
Got to get myself into it
B♭7 C7 | Fm w/riff 1 |
Why not help me do it?

Bridge 1

Fm/E♭ Fm/D
It's a chance in a lifetime
B♭7 C7 Fm
It's a chance in a lifetime
Fm/E♭ Fm/D
It's a chance in a lifetime
B♭7 C7 Fm N.C.
It's a chance in a life - time.

Verse 3

F5
Off the train

Feel insane

What the fuck

Just bad luck.

Chorus 3 As Chorus 2

Bridge 2

Fm/E♭ Fm/D
It's a chance in a lifetime

B♭7 C7 Fm
It's a chance in a lifetime

Fm/E♭ Fm/D
It's a chance in a lifetime

B♭7 C7 Fm
Don't you tell me that I'm blind

Fm/E♭ Fm/D B♭7
'Cause I'll show you that you're— blind

C7 Fm
Don't you tell me that I'm blind

Fm/E♭ Fm/D B♭7 C7 ||
'Cause I'll show you that you're— blind.

Chorus 4

N.C.(Fm)
|: Got to get myself into it

(Fm/E♭)
Got to get myself into it

(Fm/D)
Got to get myself into it

(B♭7) (C7)
Why not help me do it? :| *Play 4 times*

| **Fm(w/riff 1)** ||

Bridge 3

Fm/E♭ Fm/D
It's a chance in a lifetime

B♭7 C7 Fm
It's a chance in a lifetime

Fm/E♭ Fm/D
It's a chance of a lifetime

B♭7 C7 Fm
|: Don't you tell me that I'm blind

Fm/E♭ Fm/D
'Cause I'll show you that you're blind. :|

| **B♭7 C7** ||

Outro

w/riff 1 — **w/riff 1** —
|: **Fm** | **Fm/E♭** | **Fm/D** | **B♭7 C7** :| **Fm** (fermata) *Sax to fade*

Harrowdown Hill

Words & Music by
Thom Yorke

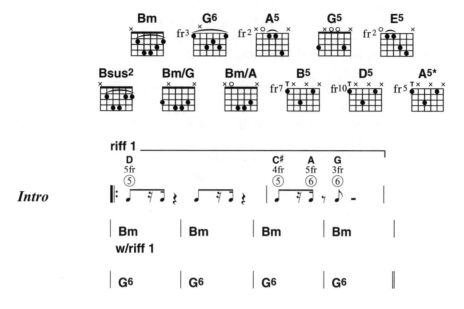

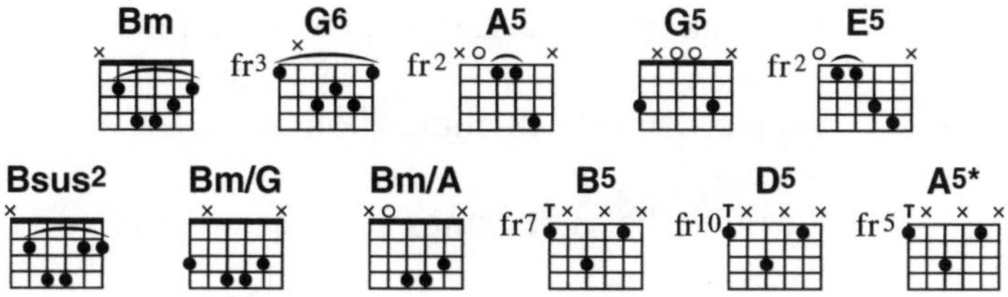

Intro

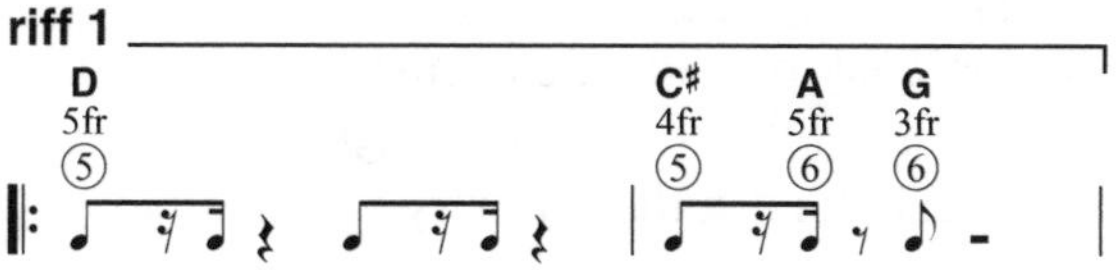

| Bm | Bm | Bm | Bm |
w/riff 1

| G6 | G6 | G6 | G6 ||

Verse 1

Bm w/riff 1
Don't walk the plank like I did

You will be dispensed with
G6
When you've become inconvenient
Bm
Up on Harrowdown Hill

Near where you used to go to school
G6
That's where I am

That's where I'm lying down
Bm
Did I fall or was I pushed?

Did I fall or was I pushed?
G6
And where's the blood?

And where's the blood?

Chorus 1

A5
But I'm coming home, I'm coming home

To make it all right, so dry your eyes
G5
We think the same things at the same time
E5
We just can't do anything about it——

We think the same things at the same time
G5
We just can't do anything about it.
A5
So don't ask me, ask the ministry
G5
Don't ask me ask the ministry

We think the same things at the same time

There are so many of us
E5
So you can't count.

We think the same things at the same time
G5
There are too many of us

So you can't count.

Link 1

| A5 | A5 | A5 | A5 |
| G5 | G5 | G5 | G5 ‖

Verse 2

Bm w/riff 1
Can you see me when I'm running?

Can you see me when I'm running?
G6
A-way from them

Away from them.
Bm
I can't take their pressure

cont.

```
No one cares if you live or die
             G6
They just want me gone

They want me gone.

         A5
But I'm coming home, I'm coming home

To make it all right, so dry your eyes
G5
We think the same things at the same time
                                E5
We just can't do anything about it___

We think the same things at the same time
G5
   There are too many of us so you can't
                                     Bm
There are too many of us so you can't count.
```

Chorus 2 (starts at "But I'm coming home")

Outro

```
| Bsus2 (fermata) | Bm (fermata) | Bsus2 (fermata) | Bm (fermata) |
                                                    w/vocal ad lib.

                Bm/G
There was a slippery slippery slippery slope
                Bm/A
There was a slippery slippery slippery slope
          E5
I feel me slipping in and out of consciousness

I feel me slipping in and out of consciousness

I feel me...

                                              1, 2.
||: B5     | B5    N.C. | B5       | D5   A5  :||

3.
| D5  A5*  | B5       ||
```

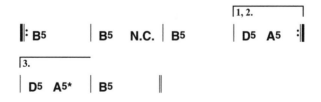

Hoppípolla

Words & Music by
Jon Birgisson, Orri Dryasson, Georg Holm & Kjartan Sveinsson

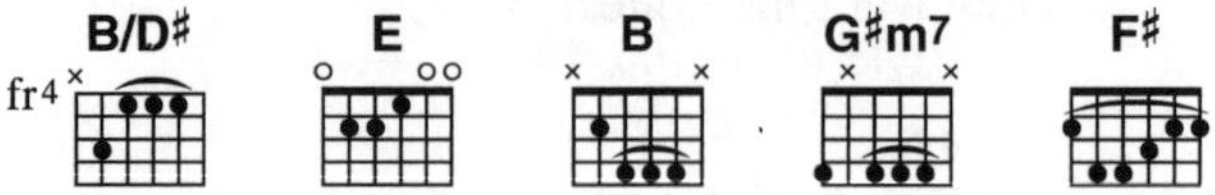

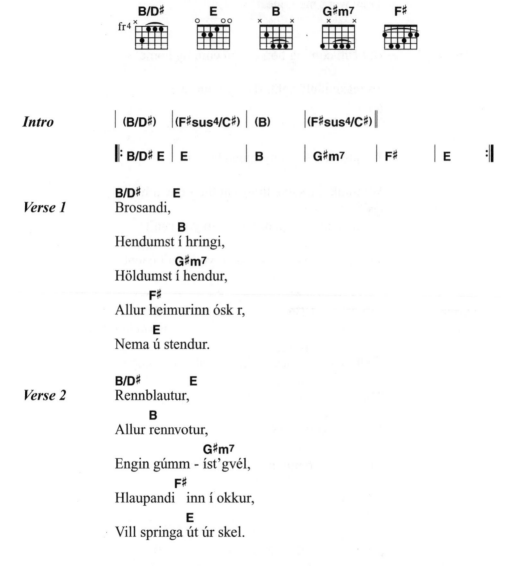

Intro | (B/D♯) | (F♯sus4/C♯) | (B) | (F♯sus4/C♯) ||

|: B/D♯ E | E | B | G♯m7 | F♯ | E :|

Verse 1

B/D♯ E
Brosandi,
B
Hendumst í hringi,
G♯m7
Höldumst í hendur,
F♯
Allur heimurinn ósk r,
E
Nema ú stendur.

Verse 2

B/D♯ E
Rennblautur,
B
Allur rennvotur,
G♯m7
Engin gúmm - íst'gvél,
F♯
Hlaupandi inn í okkur,
E
Vill springa út úr skel.

Verse 3

```
B/D#         E
Vindurinn,
  B              G#m7
Og útilykt af hárinu  ínu,
               F#
Eg lamdi eins fast og ég get,
             E
Me nefinu mínu.
```

Bridge

```
B     F#
Hoppí - polla,
            E
I engum stígvélum,
B/D#    B                   F#
   Allur rennvotur, rennblautur,
            E         F#
I engum stígvélum.
```

Chorus 1

```
             B/D#    E
Og ég fæ blónasir,
               B/D# E
En ég stend alltaf upp,

Hopelandic.

|: B     | G#m7  | F#    | E    :|
```

Chorus 2

```
             B/D#    E
Og ég fæ blónasir,
               B/D# E
En ég stend alltaf upp,

Hopelandic.
```

Outro

```
|: B     | G#m7  | F#    | E    :|   Play 4 times

| B     ||
```

Here It Goes Again

Words & Music by
Damian Kulash

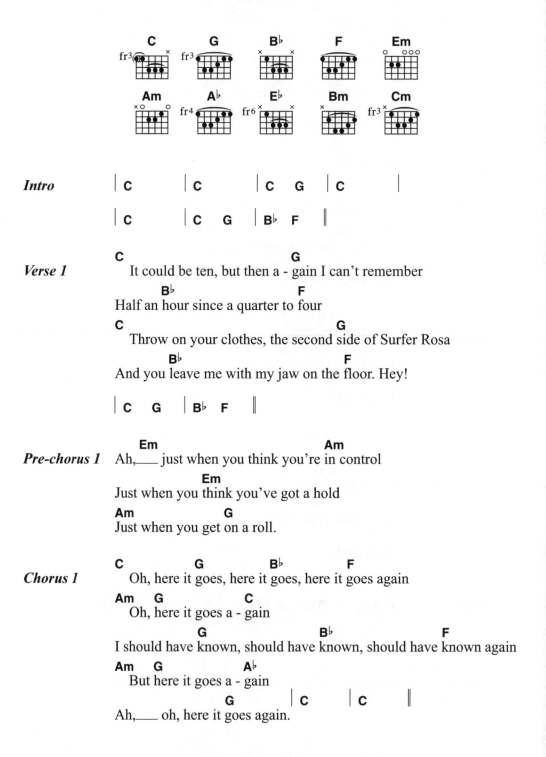

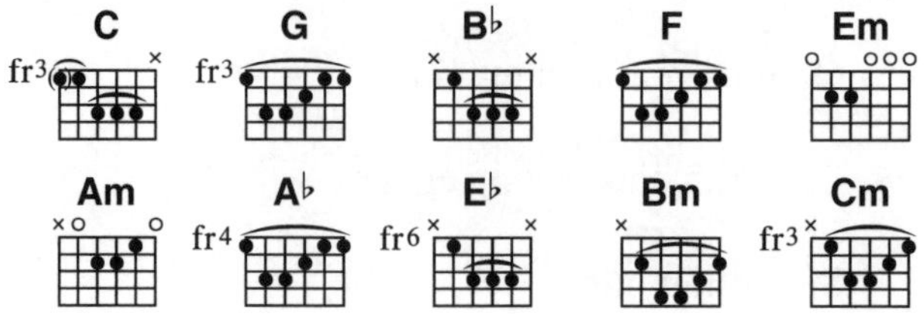

Intro

| C | C | C G | C |

| C | C G | B♭ F ‖

Verse 1

C G
It could be ten, but then a - gain I can't remember
B♭ F
Half an hour since a quarter to four
C G
Throw on your clothes, the second side of Surfer Rosa
B♭ F
And you leave me with my jaw on the floor. Hey!

| C G | B♭ F ‖

Pre-chorus 1

Em Am
Ah,___ just when you think you're in control
Em
Just when you think you've got a hold
Am G
Just when you get on a roll.

Chorus 1

C G B♭ F
Oh, here it goes, here it goes, here it goes again
Am G C
Oh, here it goes a - gain
G B♭ F
I should have known, should have known, should have known again
Am G A♭
But here it goes a - gain
G | C | C ‖
Ah,___ oh, here it goes again.

Verse 2

```
C                                     G
   It starts out easy, something simple, something sleazy
               B♭                         F
Something inching past the edge of the re - serve
C                                  G
   Now through lines of the cheap Venetian blinds
      B♭                             F
Your car is pulling off of the curb. Hey!

| C   G   | B♭   F   ||
```

Pre-chorus 2

```
     Em                                   Am
Ah,—— just when you think you're in control
                    Em
Just when you think you've got a hold
Am                    G
Just when you get on a roll.
```

Chorus 2

```
C               G              B♭              F
   Oh, here it goes, here it goes, here it goes again
Am    G                 C
   Oh, here it goes a - gain
                    G                         B♭                   F
I should have known, should have known, should have known again
Am    G                 C
   But here it goes a - gain
               G    B♭              F
Oh here it goes,     oh, here it goes
Am    G                 A♭
   Oh, here it goes a - gain
               B♭
Oh, here it goes again.
```

Solo

```
|: E♭   | E♭   | B♭   | B♭   Bm | Cm   | G   A♭ :|

| C   G   | B♭   F   | Am   G   ||
```

Verse 3

```
C                                      G
   I guess there's got to be a break in the monotony
    B♭                           F
But Jesus, when it rains how it pours
C                                                G
   Throw on your clothes, the second side of Surfer Rosa
          B♭                      F
And you leave me, yeah, you leave me.  Ah!
```

Outro-chorus

```
C               G                B♭              F
   Oh, here it goes, here it goes, here it goes again
Am     G                 C
   Oh, here it goes a - gain
                 G                          B♭                     F
I should have known, should have known, should have known again
Am     G                 C
   But here it goes a - gain
              G      B♭           F
Oh, here it goes,     oh, here it goes
Am     G                 C
   Oh, here it goes a - gain.
                 G         B♭              F
I should have known,    I should have known
Am     G                 C
   But here it goes a - gain.
              G               B♭              F
Oh, here it,    oh, here it,    oh, here it,    oh, here it
Am     G                 C
   Oh, here it goes a - gain.
                 G                   B♭                  F
I should have,    I should have,    I should have,    I should have
Am G                        C
   I  should have known.
(C)    G       B♭       F
   Oh,___ oh,___ oh, I should have known
Am     G                 A♭
   Oh, here it goes a - gain
                       B♭           E♭ (fermata)
Oh,___ oh, here it goes again.
```

In The Morning

Song by Johnny Borrell
Music by Razorlight

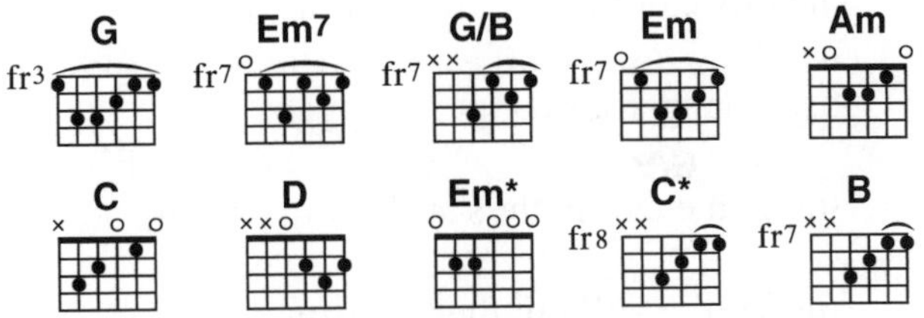

Intro | Drums 4 |: G | G | Em7 | Em7 :|

Verse 1

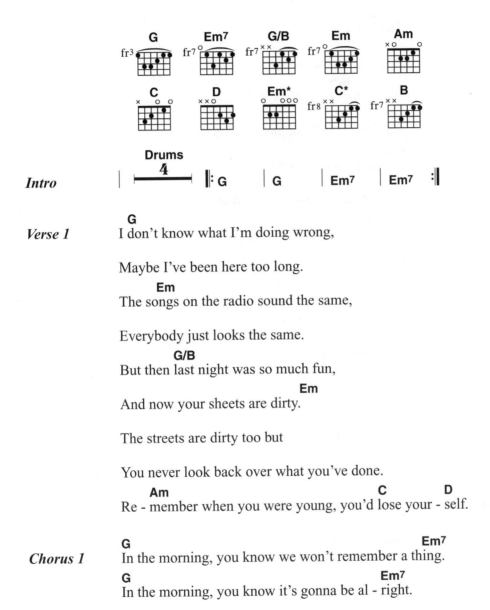

```
G
I don't know what I'm doing wrong,

Maybe I've been here too long.
      Em
The songs on the radio sound the same,

Everybody just looks the same.
       G/B
But then last night was so much fun,
                                Em
And now your sheets are dirty.

The streets are dirty too but

You never look back over what you've done.
     Am                                   C          D
Re - member when you were young, you'd lose your - self.
```

Chorus 1

```
G                                          Em7
In the morning, you know we won't remember a thing.
G                                      Em7
In the morning, you know it's gonna be al - right.
```

Verse 2

```
G
Wake him up, warm him up,

Put him on the stage. Well,
    Em
The boy can't help it, it's not his fault,

Just a dangerous dangerous age.
          G/B
But then every night's still so much fun,

And you're still out there darling,
Em
Clinging on to the wrong ideas but

I never regret anything I've done.
     Am                                        C        D
Re - member when you were young, you'd lose your - self.
```

Chorus 2

```
G                                                Em7
In the morning you know we won't remember a thing.
G                                       Em7
In the morning you know it's gonna be al - right.
C                                                  G
In the morning, you know we won't remember a thing.
C
In the morning, you know it's gonna be all...
```

Link 1

| Em* | Em* | Em | Em ||

Interlude

| Am | C D | Am | C D |

| Am | C D | Am | C D ||

```
             G                                          Em7
*Chorus 3*   In the morning, you know we won't remember a thing.
             G                                   Em*
             In the morning, you know it's gonna be all...
             C                                          G
             In the morning, you know we won't remember a thing.
             C                                   Em   D
             In the morning, you know it's gonna be al - right.

             And.


Link 2       ||: Em7   | Em7   | C*   | B   :||

                Em7
Outro        ||: Are you really gonna do it this time?

             Are you really gonna do it this time?
             C*
             Are you really gonna do it this time?
             B
             Are you really gonna do it this time? :||  Play 4 times

             Em7                                        C*
             In the morning you know we won't remember a thing,
                         B
             No, not a thing.
             Em
             In the morning you know we won't remember a thing.
```

Lonely At The Top

Words & Music by
William Brown & Samuel Preston

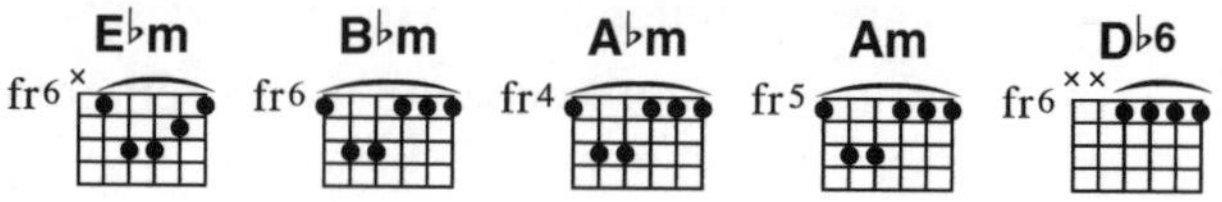

Verse 1

```
E♭m         B♭m                  E♭m
   This is a song for all of my close friends
              B♭m                      E♭m
Anonymous neighbours with stories to tell
              B♭m                A♭m
I didn't rea - lise I had so many close friends
             Am B♭m                       A♭m
Nameless and shameless with history to sell.
```

Pre-chorus 1

```
                          Am      B♭m
What's the fuss? You've gotta be in it to win it
A♭m            Am  B♭m
   I want pride but I know I'll never get it
A♭m                Am     B♭m
   Fame, I wanna live for 15 minutes
A♭m             Am    B♭m
   I want love but my heart's not in it.
```

Chorus 1

```
E♭m              B♭m          E♭m
   If only it was lonely at the top,
               B♭m                E♭m
I've got too much, but it's never e - nough
               B♭m          A♭m
If only it was lonely at the top
          Am    B♭m           E♭m
If only it was lonely at the top.
```

Link 1

```
               B♭m
Oh oh oh oh___ (Hey! Hey!)
E♭m            B♭m
   Oh oh oh oh___ ow
E♭m            B♭m
   Oh oh oh oh___ (Hey! Hey!)
         A♭m            Am    B♭m           E♭m   | E♭m | E♭m | D♭6
Na na na na, if only it was lonely at the top.
```

Verse 2

```
E♭m          B♭m                       E♭m
   This is a song for all the com - plainers
                B♭m                          E♭m
All the cam - paigners who will not give up
                        B♭m                          A♭m
They're selling their souls just to wear their sun - glasses
            Am       B♭m                  A♭m
They say "stop the press, I want to get off."
```

Pre-chorus 2

```
                                 Am      B♭m
What's the fuss? You've gotta be in it to win it
A♭m                Am  B♭m
   I want pride but I know I'll never get it
A♭m                  Am      B♭m
   Shame, I wanna live for 15 minutes
A♭m               Am     B♭m
   I want love but my heart's not in it
```

Chorus 2

```
E♭m               B♭m          E♭m
   If only it was lonely at the top
              B♭m                E♭m
I've got too much, but it's never e - nough
                B♭m         A♭m
If only it was lonely at the top
           Am    B♭m
If only it was lonely...
```

Solo

```
| E♭m     | B♭m      | E♭m       | B♭m     |
| E♭m     | EB♭m     | A♭m  Am   | B♭m     ||
```

Pre-chorus 3

```
Am                                    B♭m
   What's the fuss? You've gotta be in it to win it
A♭m                     B♭m
   I want pride but I know I'll never get it
N.C. A♭m                      B♭m
       Fame, I wanna live for 15 minutes
A♭m               Am     B♭m
   I want love but my heart's not in it.
```

Link 2

B♭m
Oh oh oh oh___ (Hey! Hey!)
E♭m B♭m
Oh oh oh oh___ ow
E♭m B♭m
Oh oh oh oh___ (Hey! Hey!)
A♭m Am B♭m
Na na na na ow, na na na na ow.

Chorus 3

E♭m B♭m E♭m
If only it was lonely at the top,
B♭m E♭m
I've got too much but it's never enough
B♭m A♭m
If only it was lonely at the top
Am B♭m E♭m
If only it was lonely at the top.

Outro

(E♭m) B♭m
Oh oh oh oh___ (Hey! Hey!)
E♭m B♭m
Oh oh oh oh___ ow
E♭m B♭m
Oh oh oh oh___ (Hey! Hey!)
A♭m Am B♭m E♭m
Na na na na, if only it was lonely at the top.

Naïve

Words & Music by
Luke Pritchard, Hugh Harris, Max Rafferty & Paul Garred

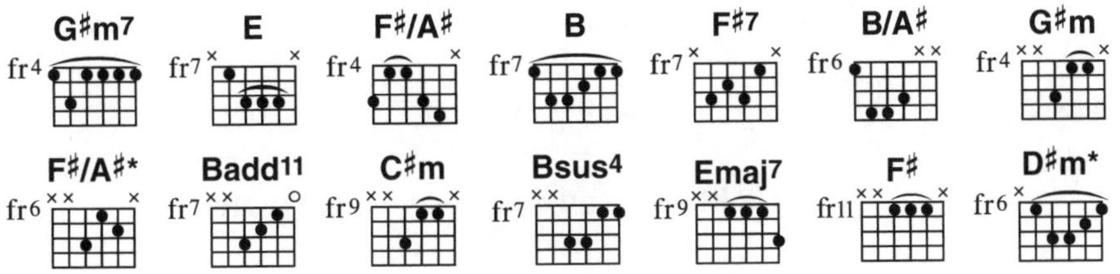

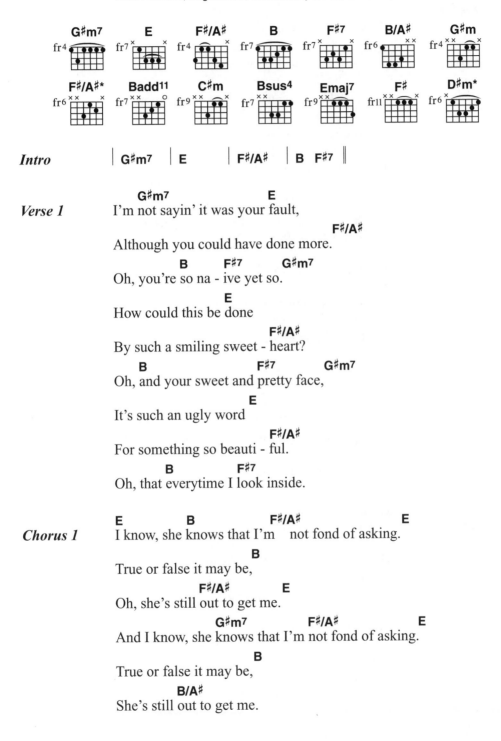

Intro | G♯m7 | E | F♯/A♯ | B F♯7 ||

Verse 1

G♯m7 E
I'm not sayin' it was your fault,
F♯/A♯
Although you could have done more.
B F♯7 G♯m7
Oh, you're so na - ive yet so.
E
How could this be done
F♯/A♯
By such a smiling sweet - heart?
B F♯7 G♯m7
Oh, and your sweet and pretty face,
E
It's such an ugly word
F♯/A♯
For something so beauti - ful.
B F♯7
Oh, that everytime I look inside.

Chorus 1

E B F♯/A♯ E
I know, she knows that I'm not fond of asking.
B
True or false it may be,
F♯/A♯ E
Oh, she's still out to get me.
G♯m7 F♯/A♯ E
And I know, she knows that I'm not fond of asking.
B
True or false it may be,
B/A♯
She's still out to get me.

Link 1 | E | E ||

Verse 2

G♯m7 E
I may say it was your fault,
F♯/A♯
Because I know you could have done more.
B F♯7 G♯m7
Oh you're so na - ive yet so.
E
How could this be done
F♯/A♯
By such a smiling sweet - heart?
B F♯7 G♯m7
Oh, and your sweet and pretty face,

It's such an ugly word
E F♯/A♯
For something so beauti - ful,
B F♯7
That everytime I look inside.

Chorus 2 As Chorus 1

Interlude

| G♯m F♯/A♯* | Badd11 C♯m | Bsus4 | Emaj7 |
| G♯m F♯/A♯* | Badd11 C♯m | F♯ | F♯ ||

Verse 3

G♯m7 E
So how could this be done
F♯/A♯
By such a smiling sweet - heart?
B F♯7 G♯m7
Oh you're so na - ive yet so.

Such an ugly thing
E F♯/A♯
For someone so beauti - ful,
B F♯7
But everytime you're on his side.

Chorus 3 As Chorus 1

Outro

```
E   D♯m*   G♯m7
              B                E   D♯m*   G♯m7
Just don't let me down.
              B
Just don't let me down

 E          D♯m*        G♯m7
𝄆 Hold on to your kite,
              B                E   D♯m*   G♯m7
Just don't let me down.
              B
Just don't let me down 𝄇

E          D♯m*        G♯m7
Hold on to this kite,
              B                E   D♯m*   G♯m7
Just don't let me down.

Just don't let me down.
```

Modern Way

Words & Music by
Nicholas Hodgson, Richard Wilson, Andrew White, James Rix & Nicholas Baines

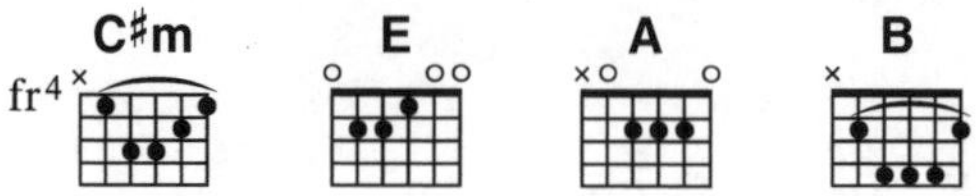

Intro | ‖: C♯m | E | A | C♯m :‖

Verse 1
C♯m E A C♯m
I know 'cause I've seen it, it was great, and I want it.
C♯m E A C♯m
There's no point in sitting going crazy on my own.
C♯m E A C♯m
Do you know what I was put here in the world for.
C♯m E A C♯m
Could you tell me in three words or more.

Bridge
B A
It's the only way of get - ting out of here
B A
It's the only way of get - ting out of here.

Verse 2
C♯m E A C♯m
Take a lesson from the ones who have been there.
C♯m E A C♯m
My brain is not damaged but in need of some re-pair.
C♯m E A C♯m
Hold on to the basics but we can change all our tactics.
C♯m E A C♯m
There's no point in sitting going crazy on your own.

Bridge
B A
It's the only way of get - ting out of here
B A
It's the only way of get - ting out of here.

Chorus
A C♯m
This is the modern way, of faking it ev'ry day,
A C♯m
And taking it as we come.
A C♯m
And we're not the only ones, is that what we used to say.
B
This is the modern way.

Interlude ‖: C♯m | E | A | C♯m :‖

Verse 3

```
C♯m                  E              A              C♯m
I know where I'm going and that we are in the knowing.
C♯m                 E                A          C♯m
And I will stop at nothing just to get what I want.
```

Bridge

```
             B                 A
It's the only way of get - ting out of here
             B                 A
It's the only way of get - ting out of here.
```

Chorus

```
    A                             C♯m
‖: This is the modern way,      of faking it ev'ry day,
A                                 C♯m
  And taking it as we come.
                                 A                          C♯m
And we're not the only ones,   is that what we used to say.
                             B
This is the modern way.        :‖
```

Outro ‖: C♯m | E | A | C♯m |

| C♯m | E | A | C♯m :‖

No Tomorrow

Words & Music by
George Astasio, Christopher Cano, Jason Pebworth,
Chad Rachild, Kevin Roentgen & John Bentjen

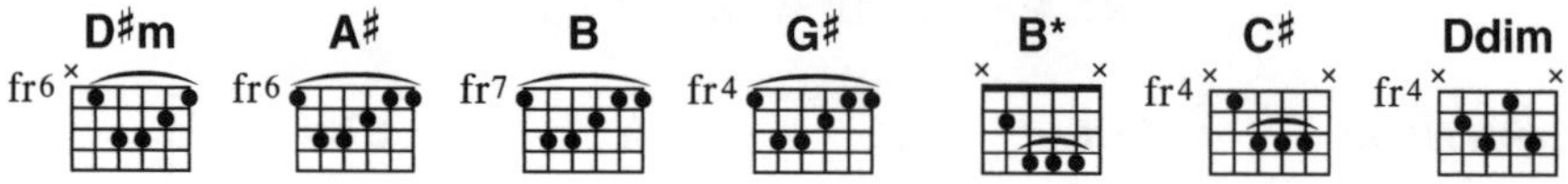

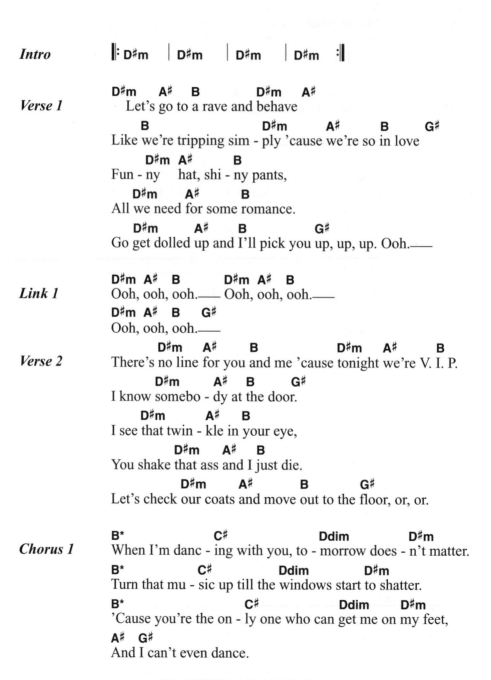

Intro ‖: D♯m | D♯m | D♯m | D♯m :‖

Verse 1
D♯m A♯ B D♯m A♯
Let's go to a rave and behave
B D♯m A♯ B G♯
Like we're tripping sim - ply 'cause we're so in love
D♯m A♯ B
Fun - ny hat, shi - ny pants,
D♯m A♯ B
All we need for some romance.
D♯m A♯ B G♯
Go get dolled up and I'll pick you up, up, up. Ooh.—

Link 1
D♯m A♯ B D♯m A♯ B
Ooh, ooh, ooh.— Ooh, ooh, ooh.—
D♯m A♯ B G♯
Ooh, ooh, ooh.—

Verse 2
D♯m A♯ B D♯m A♯ B
There's no line for you and me 'cause tonight we're V. I. P.
D♯m A♯ B G♯
I know somebo - dy at the door.
D♯m A♯ B
I see that twin - kle in your eye,
D♯m A♯ B
You shake that ass and I just die.
D♯m A♯ B G♯
Let's check our coats and move out to the floor, or, or.

Chorus 1
B* C♯ Ddim D♯m
When I'm danc - ing with you, to - morrow does - n't matter.
B* C♯ Ddim D♯m
Turn that mu - sic up till the windows start to shatter.
B* C♯ Ddim D♯m
'Cause you're the on - ly one who can get me on my feet,
A♯ G♯
And I can't even dance.

```
               D♯m  A♯  B          D♯m
Link 2         Ooh,        wh - oa,
                    A♯  B          D♯m  A♯  B  G♯
               Ooh,        wh - oa.__________

               G♯              D♯m  A♯      B
Verse 3        Ah, just look at me,    sil - ly me,
                  D♯m      A♯    B
               I'm as hap - py as could be,
                     D♯m  A♯            B     G♯
               I got a girl   who thinks I rock.
                    D♯m     A♯            B
               And tomor - row there's no school,
                         D♯m      A♯            B
               So let's go drink some more Red Bull
                          D♯m      A♯    B          G♯
               And not get home till a - bout six o' clock, oh, oh.


Chorus 2       As Chorus 1

               N.C.
Verse 4        Everybody here is staring at the outfit that you're wearing,

               Love it when they check you out.

               Cover's only twenty bucks and even if the DJ sucks,
                                               C♯  B*  C♯  Ddim  D♯m  B*  C♯  Ddim  D♯m
               It's time to turn this mother out,                     oh.___
               B*  C♯  Ddim  D♯m  B*  C♯  Ddim
               Yeah._____________________

               B*                C♯
Outro          When we're to - gether,
               Ddim              D♯m
               When we're to - gether,
               B*              C♯
               There's no to - morrow,
               Ddim            D♯m
               There's no to - morrow.
               B*                C♯
               When we're to - gether,
               Ddim              D♯m A♯  G♯
               There's no one in     the  world

               But you and me, Oh, you and me, Oh, you and me.
```

Put Your Money Where Your Mouth Is

Words & Music by
Chris Cester, Cameron Muncey & Nicholas Cester

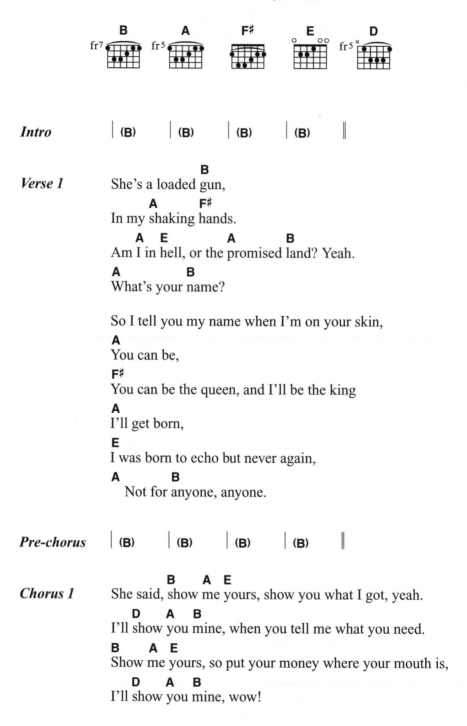

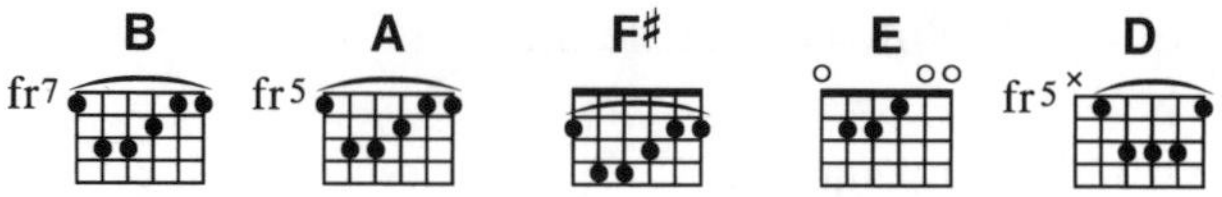

Intro | (B) | (B) | (B) | (B) ||

Verse 1

B
She's a loaded gun,
A F♯
In my shaking hands.
A E A B
Am I in hell, or the promised land? Yeah.
A B
What's your name?

So I tell you my name when I'm on your skin,
A
You can be,
F♯
You can be the queen, and I'll be the king
A
I'll get born,
E
I was born to echo but never again,
A B
Not for anyone, anyone.

Pre-chorus | (B) | (B) | (B) | (B) ||

Chorus 1

B A E
She said, show me yours, show you what I got, yeah.
D A B
I'll show you mine, when you tell me what you need.
B A E
Show me yours, so put your money where your mouth is,
D A B
I'll show you mine, wow!

Verse 2

And the beat goes on

N.C.
She knows nothin' is wrong

She goes down, like a setting sun, ow

A   B
What's your name?

If I tell you my name you gotta let me in.

A   F♯
You can be,

You can be the sinner and I'll be the sin.

A   E
I will take,

I'll take what I want, and it's easy to see,

A   B
I got everything, everything.

Chorus 2

B   A   E
She said, show me yours, show you what I got, yeah.

D   A   B
I'll show you mine, when you tell me what you need.

B   A   E
Show me yours, so put your money where your mouth is,

D   A   B
I'll show you mine, wow!

Link

| (B) | (B) | (B) | (B) ||

Guitar solo

|: B A E | E | D A B | E :|

Chorus 3

B   A   E
Show me yours, show you what I got, yeah.

D   A   B
I'll show you mine, when you tell me what you need.

B   A   E
Show me yours, so put your money where your mouth is,

D   A   B
I'll show you mine, watch out, watch out

B A E   D A B
A - ny place, any - time.

Resolve

Words & Music by
Dave Grohl, Taylor Hawkins, Nate Mendel & Chris Shiflett

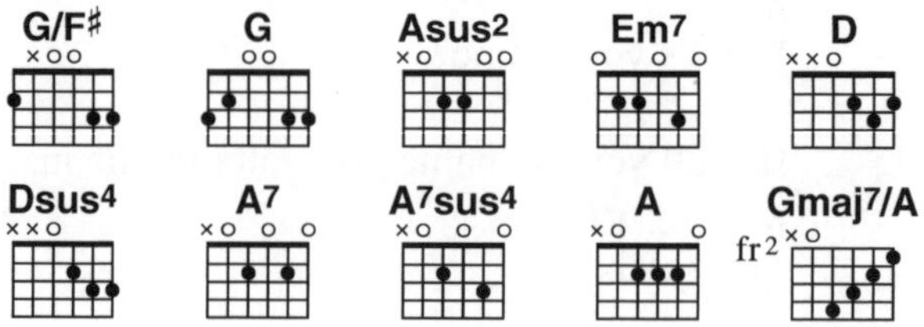

Intro

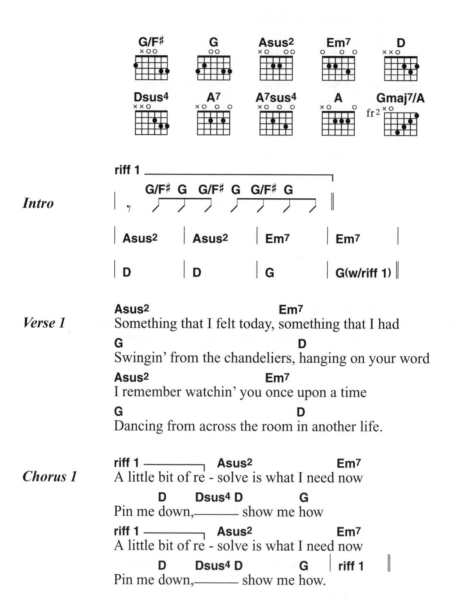

riff 1
| 𝄾 G/F♯ G G/F♯ G G/F♯ G ‖
| Asus2 | Asus2 | Em7 | Em7 |
| D | D | G | G(w/riff 1) ‖

Verse 1

Asus2 Em7
Something that I felt today, something that I had
G D
Swingin' from the chandeliers, hanging on your word
Asus2 Em7
I remember watchin' you once upon a time
G D
Dancing from across the room in another life.

Chorus 1

riff 1 Asus2 Em7
A little bit of re - solve is what I need now
D Dsus4 D G
Pin me down,——— show me how
riff 1 Asus2 Em7
A little bit of re - solve is what I need now
D Dsus4 D G | riff 1 ‖
Pin me down,——— show me how.

```
            Asus2                           Em7
Verse 2     Lookin' back to find my way, never sing so hard
            G                       D
            Yesterday's belated rest, changing of the gods
            Asus2                          Em7
            I would never change a thing even if I could
            G                                    D
            All the songs we used to sing, everything was gone.


Chorus 2    As Chorus 1

            Asus2
Bridge 1    One more hint that you're not here
               Em7
            It's gone and passed you by
                             D                    G       | riff 1   |
            It happened to you, it happened to you
            Asus2
            One more tear that you won't hear
                 Em7
            That's gone and passed you by
                             D                    G
            It happened to you, it happened to you.


Chorus 3    As Chorus 1

            riff 1 ________  Asus2
Outro       A little bit of re - solve___

            One more hint that you're not here
               Em7
            It's gone and passed you by
                               D     | D      | G      |
            A little bit of re - solve.___
            riff 1 ________  Asus2
            A little bit of re - solve___

            One more hint that you're not here
               Em7
            It's gone and passed you by
                               D     | D      | G      | riff 1   |
            A little bit of re - solve.___
            | Asus2 | A7 | A7sus4 | A | Gmaj7/A | Asus2 ||
                                        arpeggio
                                        ad lib.
```

She Moves In Her Own Way

Words & Music by
Luke Pritchard, Hugh Harris, Max Rafferty & Paul Garred

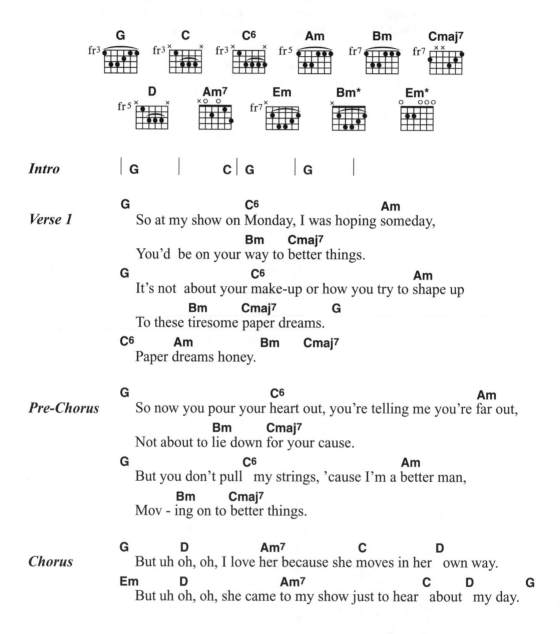

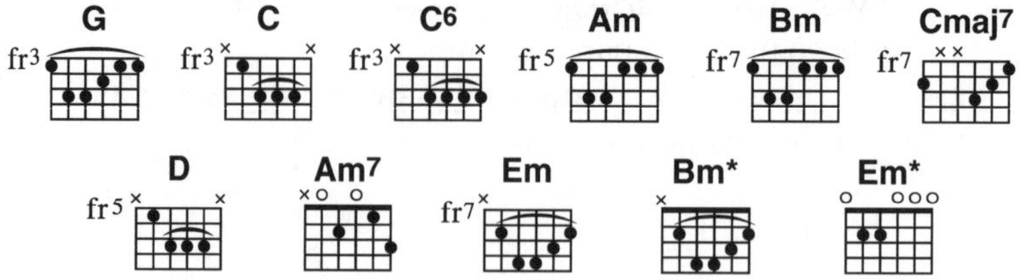

Intro | G | C | G | G |

Verse 1

G C6 Am
So at my show on Monday, I was hoping someday,
Bm Cmaj7
You'd be on your way to better things.
G C6 Am
It's not about your make-up or how you try to shape up
Bm Cmaj7 G
To these tiresome paper dreams.
C6 Am Bm Cmaj7
Paper dreams honey.

Pre-Chorus

G C6 Am
So now you pour your heart out, you're telling me you're far out,
Bm Cmaj7
Not about to lie down for your cause.
G C6 Am
But you don't pull my strings, 'cause I'm a better man,
Bm Cmaj7
Mov - ing on to better things.

Chorus

G D Am7 C D
But uh oh, oh, I love her because she moves in her own way.
Em D Am7 C D G
But uh oh, oh, she came to my show just to hear about my day.

Verse 1

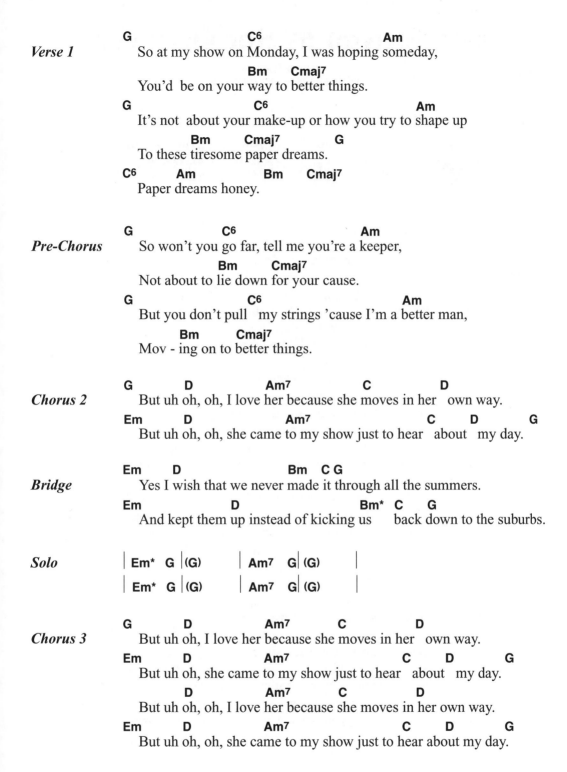

G C6 Am
So at my show on Monday, I was hoping someday,
Bm Cmaj7
You'd be on your way to better things.
G C6 Am
It's not about your make-up or how you try to shape up
Bm Cmaj7 G
To these tiresome paper dreams.
C6 Am Bm Cmaj7
Paper dreams honey.

Pre-Chorus

G C6 Am
So won't you go far, tell me you're a keeper,
Bm Cmaj7
Not about to lie down for your cause.
G C6 Am
But you don't pull my strings 'cause I'm a better man,
Bm Cmaj7
Mov - ing on to better things.

Chorus 2

G D Am7 C D
But uh oh, oh, I love her because she moves in her own way.
Em D Am7 C D G
But uh oh, oh, she came to my show just to hear about my day.

Bridge

Em D Bm C G
Yes I wish that we never made it through all the summers.
Em D Bm* C G
And kept them up instead of kicking us back down to the suburbs.

Solo

| Em* G | (G) | Am7 G | (G) |
| Em* G | (G) | Am7 G | (G) |

Chorus 3

G D Am7 C D
But uh oh, I love her because she moves in her own way.
Em D Am7 C D G
But uh oh, she came to my show just to hear about my day.
D Am7 C D
But uh oh, oh, I love her because she moves in her own way.
Em D Am7 C D G
But uh oh, oh, she came to my show just to hear about my day.

Smiley Faces

Words & Music by
Thomas Callaway & Brian Burton

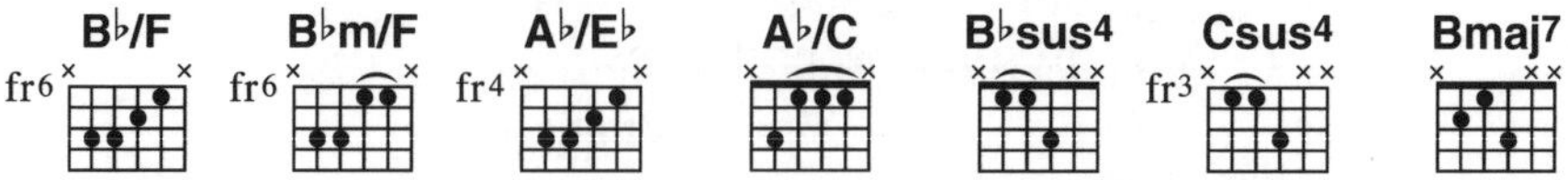

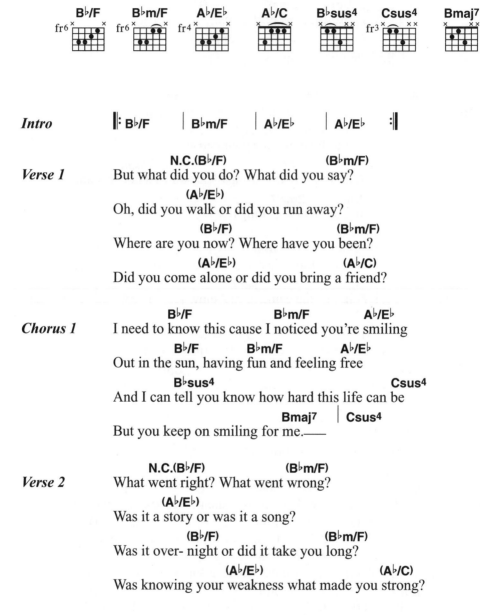

Intro ‖: B♭/F | B♭m/F | A♭/E♭ | A♭/E♭ :‖

Verse 1

```
              N.C.(B♭/F)                (B♭m/F)
But what did you do? What did you say?
              (A♭/E♭)
Oh, did you walk or did you run away?
                (B♭/F)                   (B♭m/F)
Where are you now? Where have you been?
                (A♭/E♭)                  (A♭/C)
Did you come alone or did you bring a friend?
```

Chorus 1

```
            B♭/F            B♭m/F          A♭/E♭
I need to know this cause I noticed you're smiling
             B♭/F         B♭m/F          A♭/E♭
Out in the sun, having fun and feeling free
             B♭sus4                          Csus4
And I can tell you know how hard this life can be
                              Bmaj7    | Csus4
But you keep on smiling for me.___
```

Verse 2

```
          N.C.(B♭/F)             (B♭m/F)
What went right? What went wrong?
            (A♭/E♭)
Was it a story or was it a song?
               (B♭/F)                 (B♭m/F)
Was it over- night or did it take you long?
                       (A♭/E♭)                 (A♭/C)
Was knowing your weakness what made you strong?
```

Chorus 2

```
   B♭/F                        B♭m/F          A♭/E♭
Or all the above, oh how I love to see you smiling
         B♭/F                B♭m/F       A♭/E♭
And oh yeah, take a little pain just in case
B♭sus4                                   Csus4
   You need something warm to em - brace
                                  Bmaj7
To help you put on a smiling face___
    Csus4
Hey___ you put on a smiling face.
```

Verse 3

```
N.C.(B♭m/F)                           (A♭/E♭)
   Don't you go off into the new day with any doubt
(B♭m/F)                                  (A♭/E♭)          (A♭/C)
   Here's a summary of something that you could smile about
(B♭m/F)                                (A♭/E♭)
   Say for instance my girlfriend, she bugs me all the time
(B♭m/F)                              (A♭/E♭)          (A♭/C)
   But the irony of it all is that she loves me all the time.
```

Interlude

```
 |: B♭/F      | B♭m/F     | A♭/E♭     | A♭/E♭    :|
 Oh,   see.
| B♭sus4     | B♭sus4     | Csus4      | Csus4      |

| Bmaj7      | Bmaj7      | Csus4      | Csus4      ||
```

Chorus 3

```
               B♭/F         B♭m/F          A♭/E♭
I want to leap when - ever I see you smiling
                  B♭/F              B♭m/F             A♭/E♭
Because it's easily one of the hardest things to do
B♭sus4                                     Csus4
   Your worries and fears become your friends
                                Bmaj7     | Csus4     |
And they end up smiling at you______
                    B♭/F
Put on a smiley face.___

|: (B♭/F)    | B♭m/F      | A♭/E♭      | A♭/E♭     :|

| B♭sus4     | B♭sus4     | Csus4      | Csus4      |

| Bmaj7      | Bmaj7      | Csus4      | Csus4      ||

|: N.C.(B♭/F)| (B♭m/F)    | (A♭/E♭)    | (A♭/E♭)   :|  Repeat to fade
```

Start Wearing Purple

Words & Music by
Eliot Ferguson, Eugene Hutz, Oren Kaplan, Yuri Lemeshev & Sergey Ryabstev

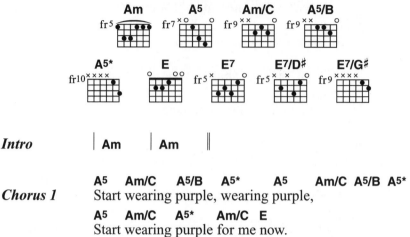

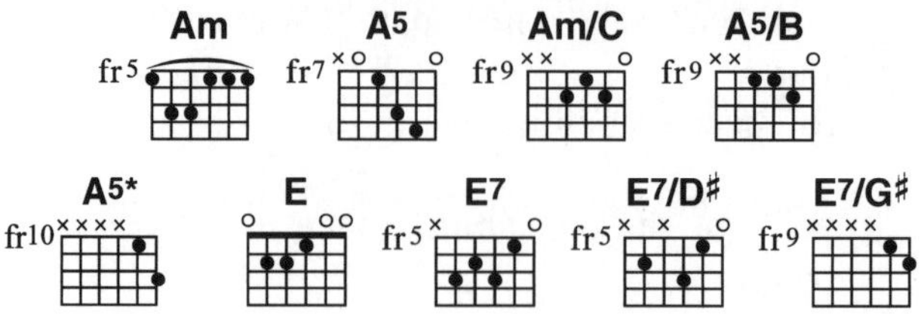

Intro | Am | Am ||

Chorus 1

A5 Am/C A5/B A5* A5 Am/C A5/B A5*
Start wearing purple, wearing purple,
A5 Am/C A5* Am/C E
Start wearing purple for me now.
E7 E7/D♯ E7/G♯ E7 E7/D♯
All your sanity and wits they will all vanish,
E7/G♯ E Am
I promise, it's just a matter of time.
N.C.
So yeah, ha.

Chorus 2

Am
Start wearing purple, wearing purple,
E
Start wearing purple for me now.

All your sanity and wits they will all vanish
Am
I promise, it's just a matter of time.

Verse 1

N.C. Am
I've known you since you were a twenty, and I was twenty,
E
And thought that some years from now

A purple little little lady will be perfect
Am
For dirty old and useless clown.
N.C.
So yeah, ha.

Chorus 3

Am
Start wearing purple, wearing purple,
                                              E
Start wearing purple for me now.

All your sanity and wits they will all vanish,
                                                  Am
I promise, it's just a matter of time.

Verse 2

N.C.   Am
I know it all from Dio - genis to Foucault
                                                E7
From Lozgechkin to Paspar - tu

I ja kljanus obostzav dva paltza
                                                    Am   N.C.
Schto muziko poshla ot Zzukov Mu!

Chorus 4

Am
Start wearing purple, wearing purple,
                                              E
Start wearing purple for me now.

All your sanity and wits they will all vanish,
                                                  Am
I promise, it's just a matter of time.
N.C.
So yeah, huh, ha, ha.

Chorus 5

Am
Start wearing purple, wearing purple,
                                              E
Start wearing purple for me now.

Link 1
(free time)

E
So why don't you start wearing purple,

Why don't you start wearing purple.
N.C.
Start wearing purple for me now!

Chorus 6 | Am | Am | Am | E ||

E
All your sanity and wits, they will all vanish,

Am
I promise, it's just a matter of time.

Link 2

N.C. Am E
So Fio-Fio-Fio - letta! Etta! Va-va-va-vaja dama ti mo - ja!

Am
Eh podayte nam karetu, votetu, i mi poedem k eben - jam!

N.C.
So yeah, ah.

Chorus 7

Am
Start wearing purple, wearing purple,

E
Start wearing purple for me now.

All your sanity and wits, they will all vanish,

Am
I promise, it's just a matter of time.

Steady, As She Goes

Words & Music by
Brendan Benson & Jack White

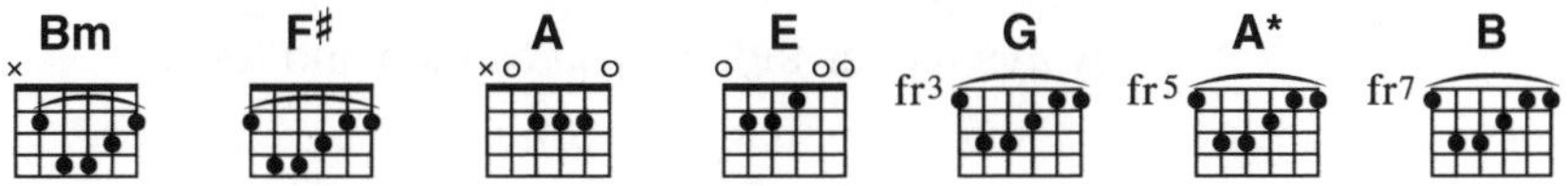

Intro

Drums

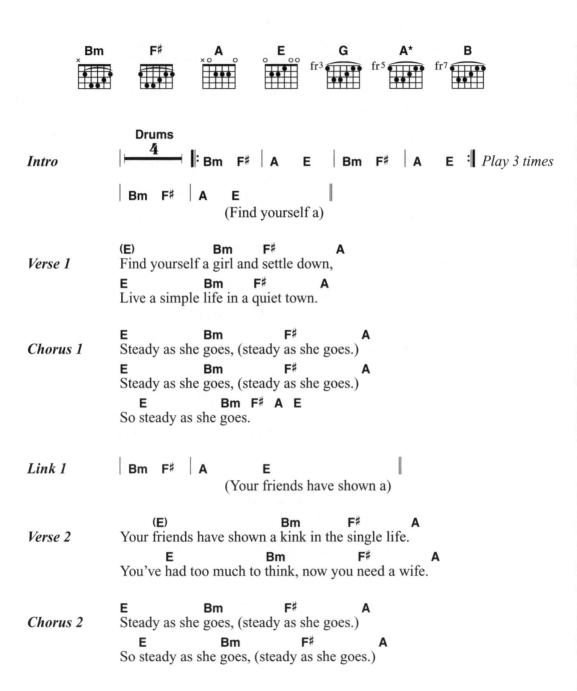

| 4 | |: Bm F♯ | A E | Bm F♯ | A E :| *Play 3 times*

| Bm F♯ | A E ||
(Find yourself a)

Verse 1

(E) Bm F♯ A
Find yourself a girl and settle down,
E Bm F♯ A
Live a simple life in a quiet town.

Chorus 1

E Bm F♯ A
Steady as she goes, (steady as she goes.)
E Bm F♯ A
Steady as she goes, (steady as she goes.)
E Bm F♯ A E
So steady as she goes.

Link 1

| Bm F♯ | A E ||
(Your friends have shown a)

Verse 2

(E) Bm F♯ A
Your friends have shown a kink in the single life.
E Bm F♯ A
You've had too much to think, now you need a wife.

Chorus 2

E Bm F♯ A
Steady as she goes, (steady as she goes.)
E Bm F♯ A
So steady as she goes, (steady as she goes.)

Bridge 1

E G
Well here we go a - gain,

A* B
You've found your - self a friend that knows you well.

A* G
But no matter what you do,

A* E
You'll always feel as though you tripped and fell.

Chorus 3

Bm F♯ A E Bm F♯ A
So steady as she goes.

Verse 3

E Bm F♯ A
When you have com - pleted what you thought you had to do,
E Bm F♯ A
And your blood's de - pleted to the point of stable glue.
E Bm F♯ A
Then you'll get a - long.
E Bm F♯ A
Then you'll get a - long.

Chorus 4

E Bm F♯ A
Steady as she goes, (steady as she goes.)
E Bm F♯ A
So steady as she goes, (steady as she goes.)

Bridge 2

E G
Well here we go a - gain,

A* B
You've found your - self a friend that knows you well.

A* G
But no matter what you do,

A* E
You'll always feel as though you tripped and fell.

Chorus 5

Bm F♯ A
So steady as she goes.
E Bm F♯
Steady as she goes.

Verse 4

```
E            Bm            F#           A
Settle for a girl, neither up or down.
E              Bm            F#              A
Sell it to the crowd that is gathered round.
E            Bm            F#           A
Settle for a girl, neither up or down.
E              Bm            F#              A   E
Sell it to the crowd that is gathered round.
```

Interlude

| Bm | Bm | Bm | Bm ||

Chorus 6

```
(Bm)              Bm            F#            A
So steady as she goes, (steady as she goes.)
E                Bm           F#          A
Steady as she goes, (steady as she goes.)
E                Bm           F#          A
Steady as she goes, (steady as she goes.)
    E             Bm            F#            A
So steady as she goes, (steady as she goes.)
```

Outro

```
E                Bm            F#          A
Steady as she goes, are you steady now?
E                Bm            F#          A
Steady as she goes, are you steady now?
E                Bm            F#          A
Steady as she goes, are you steady now?
E                Bm            F#          A
Steady as she goes, are you steady now?
E                Bm
Steady as she goes.
```

That's No Way To Tell A Lie

Words & Music by
James Dean Bradfield

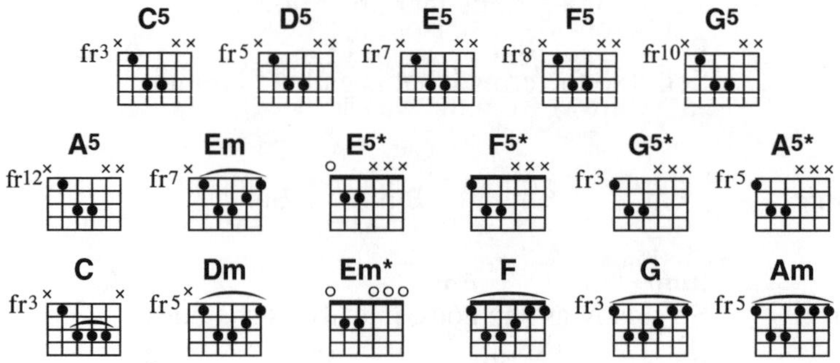

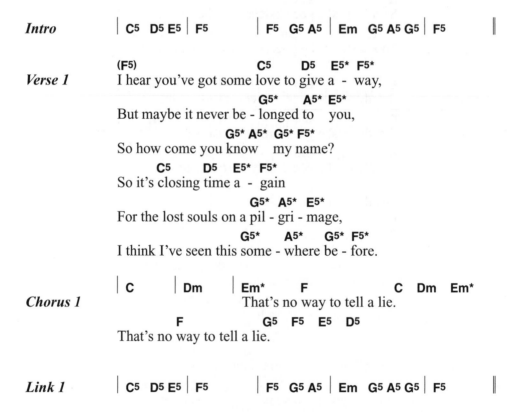

Intro | C5 D5 E5 | F5 | F5 G5 A5 | Em G5 A5 G5 | F5 ||

Verse 1
(F5) C5 D5 E5* F5*
I hear you've got some love to give a - way,
G5* A5* E5*
But maybe it never be - longed to you,
G5* A5* G5* F5*
So how come you know my name?
C5 D5 E5* F5*
So it's closing time a - gain
G5* A5* E5*
For the lost souls on a pil - gri - mage,
G5* A5* G5* F5*
I think I've seen this some - where be - fore.

Chorus 1
| C | Dm | Em* F C Dm Em*
That's no way to tell a lie.
F G5 F5 E5 D5
That's no way to tell a lie.

Link 1 | C5 D5 E5 | F5 | F5 G5 A5 | Em G5 A5 G5 | F5 ||

Verse 2

(F5) C5 D5 E5* F5*
I hear you've got some - thing to say,
G5* A5* E5*
But first you need some people to say it to,
G5* A5* G5* F5*
Just before you rise from the dead.
C5 D5 E5* F5*
So we crawl from the wa - ter's edge,
G5* A5* E5*
Returning to dip our heads a - gain,
G5* A5* G5* F5*
I'm back to where it all be - gan.

Chorus 2

| C | Dm | Em* F C Dm Em*
That's no way to tell a lie.
F G
That's no way to tell a lie.

Bridge

G Am
Sha la la la, sha la la la, sha la la la, sha la la la,
F C
Sha la la la, sha la la la, sha la la la, sha la la la.
G Am
Sha la la la, sha la la la, sha la la la, sha la la la,
F G G5 F5 E5 D5
Sha la la la, sha la la la, sha la la la.

Chorus 3

| C | Dm | Em* F C Dm Em*
That's no way to tell a lie.
F C Dm Em*
That's no way to tell a lie.
F C Dm Em*
That's no way to tell a lie.
F G G5 F5
That's no way to tell a lie.

Verse 3

E5 D5 C5 D5 E5* F5*
I hear you've got some - thing to say,
G5* A5* E5*
But first you need some people to say it to,
G5* A5* G5* F5*
Just before you rise from the dead.

Outro

C5 D5 E5 F5 G5 A5 Em G5 A5
Sha la la la, sha la la la, sha la la la, sha la la la,
G5 F5 F5 E5 D5 C
Sha la la la, sha la la la.

Turn Into

Words & Music by
Nicholas Zinner, Brian Chase & Karen Orzolek

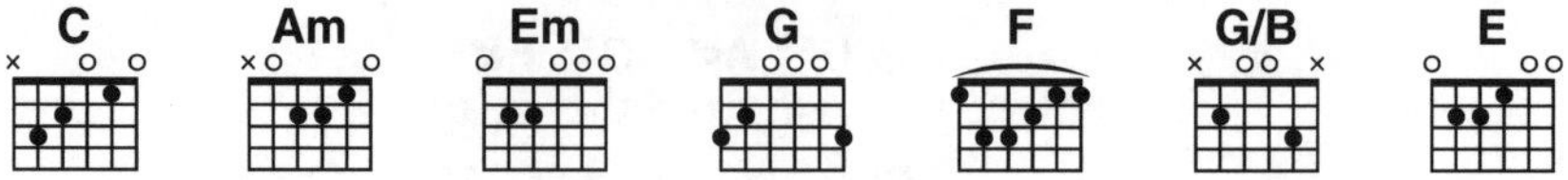

Intro | C | C | C | C ||

Verse 1

```
 C             Am      Em
I know, what I know, I know
        G
On the car ride down.
 C                      Am
I hear it in my head real low.
Em           G              C
Turn into the only thing I ever,
Am
Turn into,
Em
Hope I do,
      G
Turn into you.
```

Verse 2

```
 C             Am      Em
I know, what I know, I know,
      G
That girl you found
C                            Am
Keeps that kind of window closed.
       Em           G                C
She'll turn into the only thing you ever
Am
Turn into,
Em
Hope I do,
      G
Turn into you.
```

```
Interlude   | Am    | Am    | F     | F     |

            | C     | G/B   | F     | F     ||

            Am
Bridge      Can't say why I kept this from you,
            F
            My those quiet eyes become you.
            C                  G/B
            Leave it where it can't remind us,
            G
            Turn this all around behind us.
            Am          F
            Oh! well I know
                        C
            Well I'll fall right in to keep you out,
                E
            I'd like to tell you all about it.

Solo        |: C    | C     | Am    | Am    |

            | Em    | Em    | G     | G     :|

Link 1      | C     | C     | C     | C     ||

              C             Am      Em
Verse 3     I know, what I know, I know,
                 G
            This last time around,
                C                     Am
            I'll hear it in my head real low.
            Em          G
            Turn into the only thing you ever know.

Link 2      | C     | C     | Am    | Am    | Em    | Em    ||
                G                         C   Am   Em   G
            The only thing you ever know.

              C             Am      Em
Outro       I know, what I know, I know
                G
            Ah yes.
```

Talk

Words & Music by
Guy Berryman, Jon Buckland, Will Champion, Chris Martin,
Ralf Hütter, Karl Bartos & Emil Schult

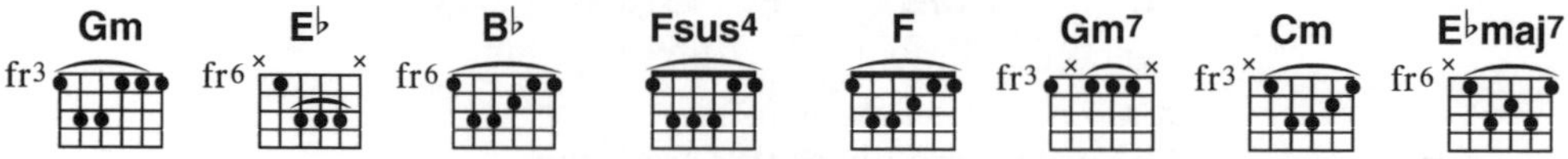

(2 bar count in)

Intro

```
||: Gm        | Gm        | Gm        | Gm       :||
 | E♭         | Gm   B♭   | E♭        | Gm   B♭   |
 | E♭         | Gm   B♭   | E♭        | Fsus4  F  ||
```

Verse 1

```
E♭                Gm      B♭         E♭        Gm  B♭
   Oh, brother I can't, I can't get through,______
            E♭           Gm
I've been trying hard to reach you
B♭      E♭                   Fsus4  F
'Cos I don't know what to do.______
E♭                Gm         B♭          E♭    Gm  B♭
   Oh, brother I can't be - lieve it's true,______
           E♭                 Gm
I'm so scared about the future
B♭      E♭              Fsus4  F
And I want to talk to you,_____
         E♭             Fsus4  F
Oh, I want to talk to you._____
```

Instrumental 1

```
| Gm        | Gm        | Gm        | Gm        ||
```

Chorus 1

```
                   E♭                Gm7              B♭  E♭  Gm7  B♭
You could take a picture of something you see,
E♭               Gm7          B♭  E♭  Gm7  B♭
In the future where will I be?
                  E♭              Gm7  B♭  E♭  Gm7  B♭
You could climb a ladder up to the sun,
    E♭             Gm7       B♭
Or write a song no - body had sung
    E♭                  Fsus4      F
Or do something that's never been done.
```

Instrumental 2 | Gm7 | Gm7 | Gm7 | Gm7 ||

Verse 2

```
E♭         Gm    B♭       E♭      Gm  B♭
   Are you lost or incom - plete?
            E♭        Gm      B♭
Do you feel like a puzzle;
              E♭             Fsus4  F
You can't find your missing piece?—
            E♭       Gm  B♭  E♭  Gm  B♭
Tell me how you feel,—
          E♭             Gm      B♭  E♭                   Fsus4  F
Well, I feel like they're talking in a language I don't speak,—
                E♭           Fsus4  F
And they're talking it to me.—
```

Instrumental 3 | Gm | Gm | Gm | Gm ||

Chorus 2

```
                      E♭               Gm7              B♭  E♭  Gm7  B♭
So you could take a picture of something you see,
E♭               Gm7          B♭  E♭  Gm7  B♭
In the future where will I be?
                  E♭              Gm7  B♭  E♭  Gm7  B♭
You could climb a ladder up to the sun,
    E♭             Gm7       B♭
Or write a song no - body had sung
                        Fsus4      F
Or do something that's never been done,
E♭                  Fsus4      F
Do something that's never been done.
```

Instrumental 4 | Gm7 | Gm7 | Gm7 | Gm7 |

|: Cm | E♭ | Gm | F |

| Cm | E♭ | Gm | F :|

Guitar solo | E♭ | Gm B♭ | E♭ | Gm B♭ |

| E♭ | Gm B♭ | E♭ | Fsus4 F ||

Chorus 3

```
              E♭
So you don't know where you're going
              Gm7      B♭  E♭  Gm7  B♭
And you want to talk,
     E♭
You feel like you're going
                    Gm7        B♭  E♭  Gm7  B♭
Where you've been be - fore,
                 E♭
You'll tell anyone who'll listen
             Gm7      B♭  E♭  Gm7  B♭
But you feel ig - nored,
     E♭                                 Gm7     B♭
And nothing's really making any sense at all.
      E♭       F
Let's talk, let's talk,
      E♭maj7   F    Gm
Let's talk, let's talk.
```

Wasted Little DJ's

Words & Music by
Kyle Falconer & Keiren Webster

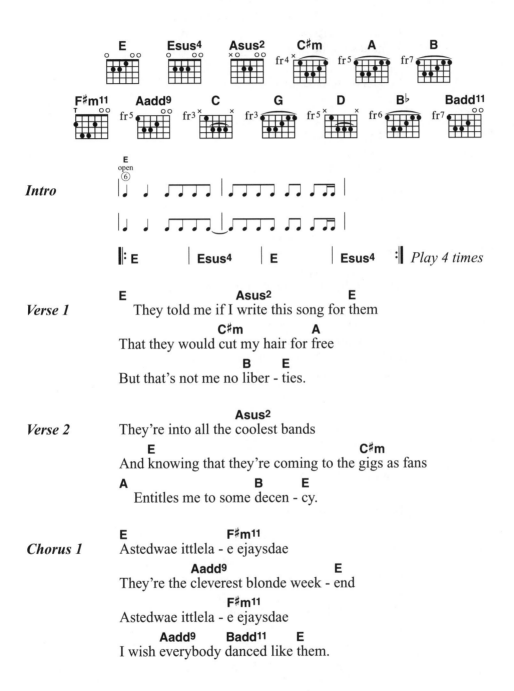

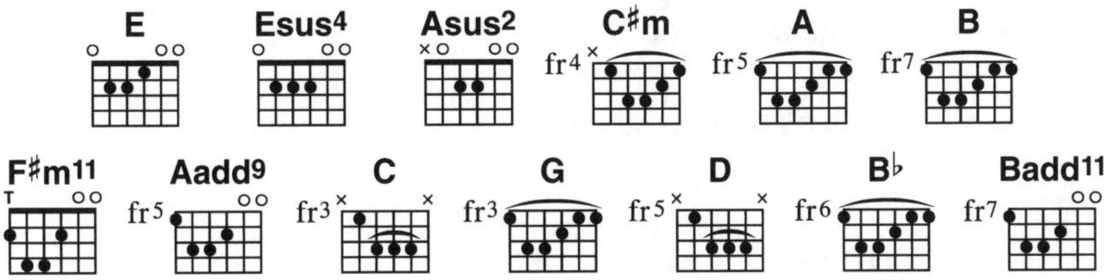

Intro

𝄆 E | Esus4 | E | Esus4 𝄇 *Play 4 times*

Verse 1

E Asus2 E
They told me if I write this song for them
C♯m A
That they would cut my hair for free
B E
But that's not me no liber - ties.

Verse 2

Asus2
They're into all the coolest bands
E C♯m
And knowing that they're coming to the gigs as fans
A B E
Entitles me to some decen - cy.

Chorus 1

E F♯m11
Astedwae ittlela - e ejaysdae
Aadd9 E
They're the cleverest blonde week - end
F♯m11
Astedwae ittlela - e ejaysdae
Aadd9 Badd11 E
I wish everybody danced like them.

Link 1 | E | Esus4 | E | Esus4 ||

Verse 3

```
E                    Asus2        E
   Split visions of a talkative thera - py
            C#m                   A
It makes me bend away it gives me E
                      B    E
Seems hard to say, its in - sani - ty.
```

Verse 4

```
                         Asus2
The same record for the 16th time
     E                        C#m
Ex - act same set you did the last time round
A                          B       E
   Doesn't bother me we're in harmo - ny.
```

Chorus 2

```
E                 F#m11
Astedwae ittlela - e ejaysdae
            Aadd9               E
They're the cleverest blonde week - end
                  F#m11
Astedwae ittlela - e ejaysdae
       Aadd9      Badd11    C#m
I wish everybody danced like them.
Aadd9      Badd11      E
Everybody danced like them.
```

Bridge

```
C        G                   D
   No low emotions rolling to - night
              A                C
Young heavy hopefuls staying the night
         G                     A   Bb  | B   Bb |
So stick around and wait for the day___
A                       Bb B              B  Bb
Craziness kills laziness and happiness takes bad bets
A                          Bb   B                   Bb
No one gives a fuck you see we're all out of our little heads
A                    Bb       B              B  Bb
Craziness kills lazi - ness and happiness takes bad bets
A                          Bb    B      B  Bb
No one gives a fuck you see we're all out of ou - r
B           B  Bb B  Bb B Bb B  Bb B    E
All out of ou - r,  all out of our lit - tle fucking heads.
```

```
            (E)                  Esus4
Link 2      Doo doo doo doo...

            | E       | C#m     | Aadd9   | Aadd9  Badd11 ||

            ||: E     | Esus4   | E       | Esus4   :||


Solo        ||: E     | Asus2   | E       | C#m     |

            | Aadd9   | Aadd9  Badd11 | E  | E       :||


               E                  F#m11
Outro-chorus   Astedwae ittlela - e ejaysdae
                                Aadd9                E
               They're the cleverest blonde weekend
                                  F#m11
               Astedwae ittlela - e ejaysdae
                          Aadd9      Badd11     E
               I wish everybody danced like them.
               E                  F#m11
               Astedwae ittlela - e ejaysdae
                                Aadd9                E
               They're the cleverest blonde weekend
                                  F#m11
               Astedwae ittlela - e ejaysdae
                          Aadd9      Badd11     E      C#m
               I wish everybody danced like them.
                      Aadd9    Badd11     E
               ||: Can anybody dance like them
                      C#m
               Can u tell me. :|| Play 3 times

                      Aadd9    Badd11     E      C#m
               Can anybody dance like them.
                     Aadd9     Badd11 E       C#m
               ||: Astedwae ittlelae ejays - dae :||

               | A   B   | E  C#m  | A   B   | E  Esus4  E(fermata) ||
               Slower
```

The W.A.N.D.

Words & Music by
Wayne Coyne, Steven Drozd & Michael Ivans

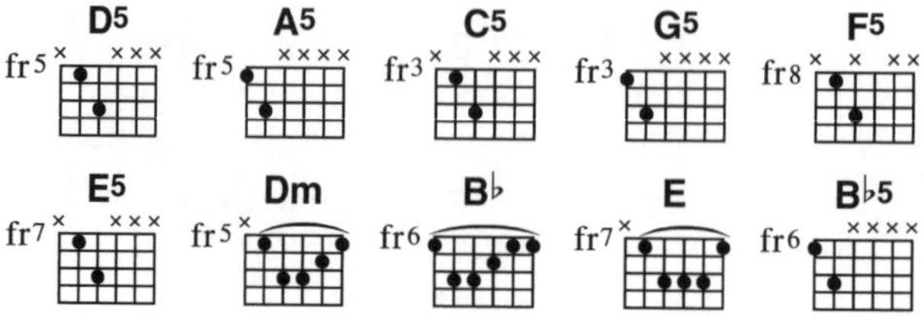

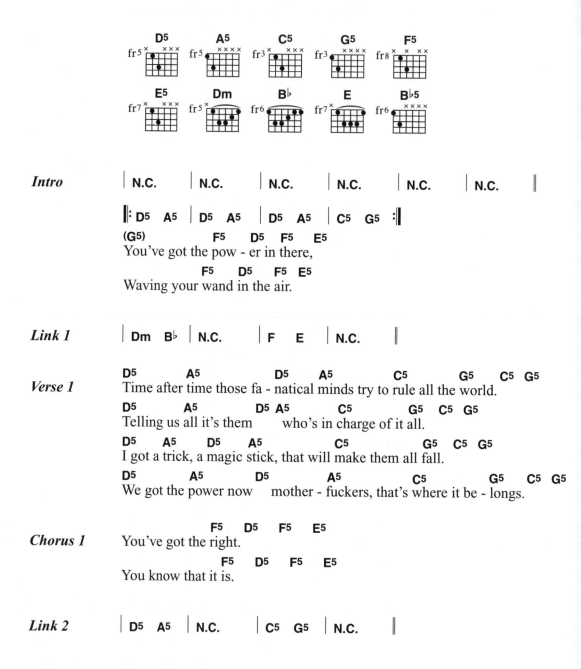

Intro | N.C. | N.C. | N.C. | N.C. | N.C. | N.C. ||

|: D5 A5 | D5 A5 | D5 A5 | C5 G5 :|

(G5) F5 D5 F5 E5
You've got the pow - er in there,
F5 D5 F5 E5
Waving your wand in the air.

Link 1 | Dm B♭ | N.C. | F E | N.C. ||

Verse 1
D5 A5 D5 A5 C5 G5 C5 G5
Time after time those fa - natical minds try to rule all the world.
D5 A5 D5 A5 C5 G5 C5 G5
Telling us all it's them who's in charge of it all.
D5 A5 D5 A5 C5 G5 C5 G5
I got a trick, a magic stick, that will make them all fall.
D5 A5 D5 A5 C5 G5 C5 G5
We got the power now mother - fuckers, that's where it be - longs.

Chorus 1
F5 D5 F5 E5
You've got the right.
F5 D5 F5 E5
You know that it is.

Link 2 | D5 A5 | N.C. | C5 G5 | N.C. ||

Verse 2

D5 A5 D5 A5
They got their weapons to solve all their questions,
C5 G5 C5 G5
They don't know what they're for.
D5 A5 D5 A5
Why can't they see that's not power, that's greed
C5 G5 C5 G5
To just want more and more.
D5 A5 D5 A5 C5 G5 C5 G5
I got a plan and it's here in my hand, a ba - ton made of light.
D5 A5 D5 A5
We're the en - forcers, the sorcerer's orphans
C5 G5 C5 G5
And we know why we fight.

Chorus 2

F5 D5
You got the right.
N.C.
You've got the power in there,
(F) (E)
Waving your wand in the air.

Link 3

‖: D5 A5 | D5 A5 | D5 A5 | C5 G5 :‖

Bridge

F5
You've got the power in there,
G5
You've got the power in there,
A5
You've got the power in there,
B♭5
Waving your wand in the air.

Chorus 3

F5 D5 F5 E5
You've got the right.
F5 D5 F5 E5
You know that it is.

When You Were Young

Words & Music by
Brandon Flowers, Dave Keuning, Mark Stoermer & Ronnie Vannucci

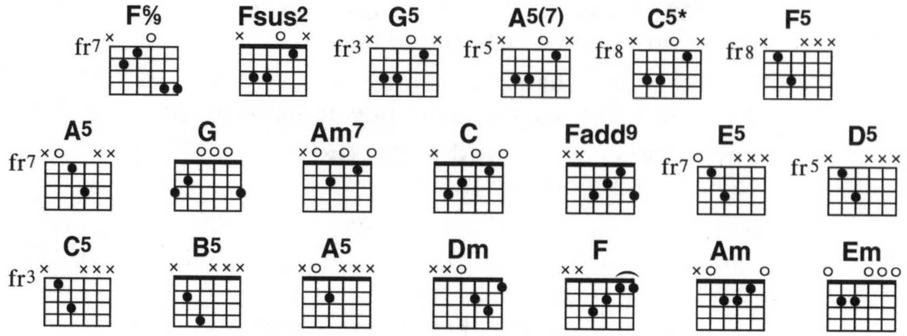

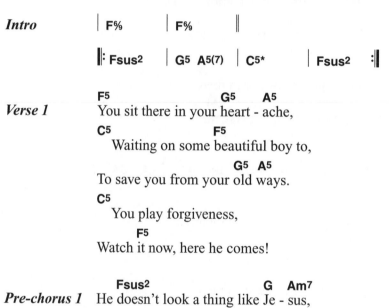

Tune guitar down a semitone

Intro | F% | F% ‖

‖: Fsus2 | G5 A5(7) | C5* | Fsus2 :‖

Verse 1

```
F5                   G5    A5
You sit there in your heart - ache,
C5                F5
   Waiting on some beautiful boy to,
                       G5  A5
To save you from your old ways.
C5
   You play forgiveness,
      F5
Watch it now, here he comes!
```

Pre-chorus 1

```
   Fsus2                   G   Am7
He doesn't look a thing like Je - sus,
          C
But he talks like a gentleman,
Fadd9
Like you imagined.
```

Chorus 1

```
      Fsus2   G5      A5(7) C5* Fsus2
When you were young.
```

Verse 2

F5
Can we climb this mountain?
G5 A5
I don't know,
C5 F5
Higher now than ever before,
G5 A5
I know we can make it if we take it slow.
C5
That's takin' easy,
F5
Ea - sy now, watch it go!

Pre-chorus 2

Fsus2 G Am7
We're burning down the highway sky - line,
C Fadd9
On the back of a hurricane that started turning,

Chorus 2

Fsus2 G5 A5(7) C5* Fsus2
When you were young.
Fsus2 G5 A5(7) C5* Fsus2
When you were young.

Bridge

Fsus2 G
And sometimes you close your eyes,
Am7 C Fadd9
And see the place where you used to live,
Fsus2 G5
When you were young..

Instr.

|: Fsus2 | G5 A5(7) | C5* | Fsus2 :|

| F5 E5 D5 | C5 B5 A5 | G5 | G5 ||

Middle 8

Dm
They say the devil's water, it ain't so sweet,
F Am
You don't have to drink right now,
Em Am
But you can dip your feet,
G
Every once in a little while.

Link |: Fsus2 | G5 A5(7) | C5 | Fsus2 :|

Verse 3

```
F5                        G5      A5
You sit there in your heart - ache,
C5                      F5
   Waiting on some beautiful boy to,
                            G5  A5
To save you from your old ways.
C5
   You play forgiveness,
        F5
Watch it now, here he comes!
```

Pre-chorus 3

```
    Fsus2                        G    Am7
He doesn't look a thing like Je - sus,
        C
But he talks like a gentleman,
Fadd9
Like you imagined.
```

Chorus 3

```
       Fsus2      G5       A5(7)
When you were young.
C5                           Fsus2
   Talks like a gentlemen, like you imagined,
       Fsus2      G5       A5(7) C5 Fsus2
When you were young.
                                     G5  A5(7) C5
I said he doesn't look a thing like Je - sus,
Fsus2                                G5  A5(7) C5
   He doesn't look a thing like Je - sus
Fsus2
   But more than you'll ever know
```

Outro | F5 E5 D5 | C5 B5 A5 | G5 ||

Wolf Like Me

Words & Music by
Tunde Adebimpe & David Sitek

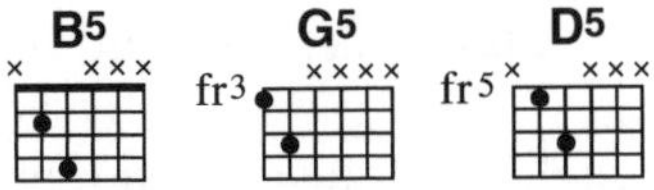

Intro | Drums 4 || B5 | B5 | B5 | B5 |
| G5 | G5 | D5 | D5 ||

Verse 1
B5
Say say my playmate, won't you lay hands on me.
G5 D5
Mirror my malady, transfer my tragedy.
B5
Got a curse I cannot lift, shines when the sunset shifts
G5 D5
When the moon is round and full, gotta bust that box, gotta gut that fish.
B5
(My mind's a - flame.)

We could jet in a stolen car, but I bet we wouldn't get too far.
G5 D5
Before the transformation takes and bloodlust tanks and crave gets slaked.

Chorus 1
B5
My mind has changed,

My body's frame but God I like it.
G5
My hearts a - flame,
D5
My body's strained but God I like it.
B5
My mind has changed,

My body's frame but God I like it
G5
My hearts a - flame
D5
My body's strained but God I like it.

Verse 2

```
B5
   Charge me your day rate, I'll turn you out in kind.
G5
   When the moon is round and full,
       D5                                        B5
Gonna teach you tricks that'll blow your mongrel mind.

Baby doll I recognize, you're a hideous thing inside.
G5                                   D5
  If ever there were a lucky kind it's you, you, you, you.
```

Chorus 2

```
            B5
I know its strange, another way to get to know you.
             G5                              D5
You'll never know unless we go, so let me show you.
             B5
I know it's strange, another way to get to know you.
              G5                                     D5
We've got till noon, here comes the moon, so let it show you.

Show you now.
```

Link 1
(half time feel)

```
| B5   | B5   | B5   | B5   |
| G5   | G5   | D5   | D5   ||
```

Bridge

```
B5
  Dream me, oh dreamer down to the floor.
G5                              D5
  Open my hands and let them weave onto yours.
B5
  Feel me, completer, down to my core.
G5                         D5
  Open my heart and let it bleed onto yours.
B5
  Feeding on fever, down all fours,
G5                        D5
  Show you what all that howl is for.
```

Link 2
(a tempo)

| B5 | B5 | B5 | B5 |
| G5 | G5 | D5 | D5 ||

Verse 3

```
B5
   Hey hey my playmate, let me lay waste to thee.
G5                                 D5
   Burned down their hanging trees, it's hot, hot, hot, hot here.
B5
   Got a curse we cannot lift, shines when the sunshine shifts.
G5                                  D5
   There's a curse comes with a kiss, the bite that binds the gift that gives.
B5
   Now that we got gone for good writhing under your riding hood.
G5                                      D5
   Tell your gra'ma and your mama too, it's true, true, true, true
```

Outro

```
     B5
We're howling forever. Oh, oh.
     G5            D5
We're howling forever. Oh, oh.
     B5
We're howling forever. Oh, oh.
     G5            D5
We're howling forever. Oh, oh.
     N.C.                B5
We're howling forever. Oh, oh.
```

Woman

Words & Music by
Andrew Stockdale, Chris Ross & Myles Heskett

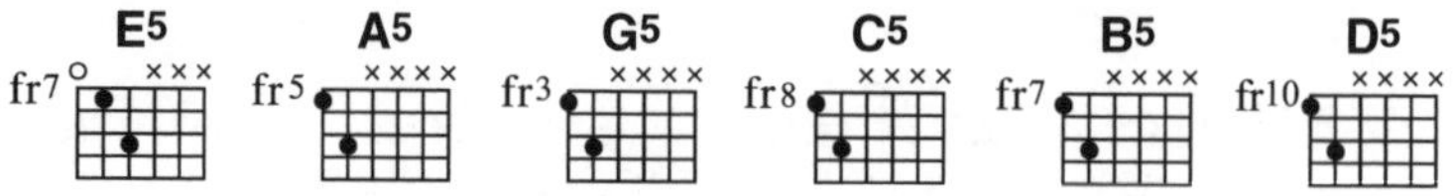

Intro ‖: E5 | E5 | E5 | A5 G5 :‖

Verse 1

E5
Woman, you know you, woman,

You gotta be a woman,
A5 G5
I've got the feeling of love.
E5
When you're, you're talking to me, you see right through me,
A5 G5
I've got the feeling of love.

Chorus 1

A5 C5 A5
She's a woman, you know what I mean,
C5 B5
You better listen, listen to me, yeah.
D5
She's gonna set you free, yeah, yeah, yeah.

Link 1 | E5 | E5 | E5 | A5 G5 ‖

Verse 2

E5
You come looking at me, like I've got to set you free,
A5 G5
I can't free no - body.
E5
You come looking at me, like I've got to set you free,
A5 G5
I can't be no - body.

Chorus 2	As Chorus 1			
Bridge	‖: N.C. A5	N.C. E5	N.C. A5	N.C. E5 :‖
	E5 D5 E5 D5	E5 D5 E5	E5 D5 E5 D5	E5 D5 E5 ‖
				Play 6 times
	‖: E5 D5 E5 D5	E5 D5 E5	E5 D5 E5 D5	E5 D5 E5 :‖
	E5 D5 E5 D5	E5 D5 E5	E5 A5	A5 G5 ‖
	E5	E5	E5	A5 G5 ‖
Verse 3	As Verse 1			
Chorus 3	As Chorus 1			
Chorus 3	N.C. A5	N.C. E5 ‖		

Relative Tuning

The guitar can be tuned with the aid of pitch pipes or dedicated electronic guitar tuners which are available through your local music dealer. If you do not have a tuning device, you can use relative tuning. Estimate the pitch of the 6th string as near as possible to E or at least a comfortable pitch (not too high, as you might break other strings in tuning up). Then, while checking the various positions on the diagram, place a finger from your left hand on the:

5th fret of the E or 6th string and **tune the open A** (or 5th string) to the note **(A)**

5th fret of the A or 5th string and **tune the open D** (or 4th string) to the note **(D)**

5th fret of the D or 4th string and **tune the open G** (or 3rd string) to the note **(G)**

4th fret of the G or 3rd string and **tune the open B** (or 2nd string) to the note **(B)**

5th fret of the B or 2nd string and **tune the open E** (or 1st string) to the note **(E)**

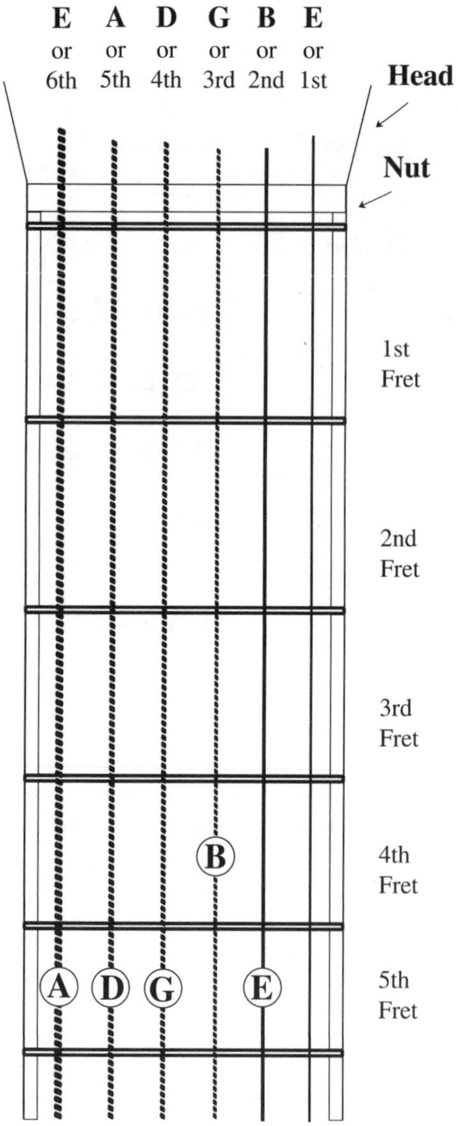

Reading Chord Boxes

Chord boxes are diagrams of the guitar neck viewed head upwards, face on as illustrated. The top horizontal line is the nut, unless a higher fret number is indicated, the others are the frets.

The vertical lines are the strings, starting from E (or 6th) on the left to E (or 1st) on the right.

The black dots indicate where to place your fingers.

Strings marked with an O are played open, not fretted. Strings marked with an X should not be played.

The curved bracket indicates a 'barre' - hold down the strings under the bracket with your first finger, using your other fingers to fret the remaining notes.

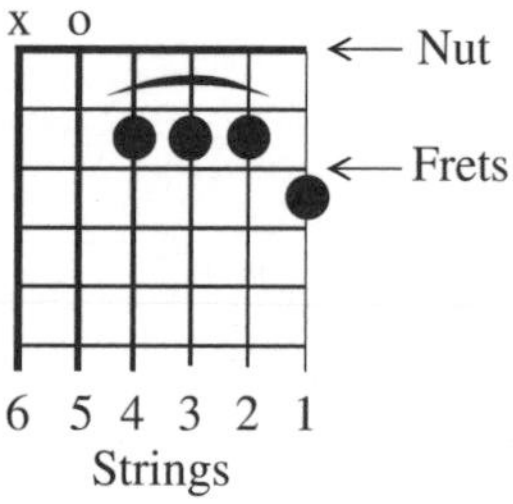

1 2 3 4 5 6 7 8 9